HIGH NOON

The publishers would like to thank the team
at IPC Media Ltd and DC Comics for their
help in compiling this book, particularly
David Abbott and Linda Lee.

Published in 2008 by Prion
An imprint of the Carlton Publishing Group
20 Mortimer Street
London W1T 3JW

A catalogue record for this book is
available from the British Library.

ISBN 978-1-85375-672-6

Printed and bound in Thailand
10 9 8 7 6 5 4 3 2 1

HIGH NOON

13 OF THE BEST
WILD WEST
PICTURE LIBRARY
STORIES EVER

GENERAL EDITOR
STEVE HOLLAND

PRION

CONTENTS

INTRODUCTION

The popularity of the Western has ebbed and flowed over the last few decades. Just when you think the cowboy has finally ridden off into the sunset, a new movie appears— *Dances With Wolves*, *Brokeback Mountain*, *3:10 To Yuma*—

that proves the Western is still alive and kicking (and who can think of three more diverse films in the same *genre*?)

It is not so long since the Western was the most popular kind of comic strip you could create.

Buck Jones, Tim Holt and Gene Autry were the top stars of Saturday morning cinema shows; Roy Rogers and Tex Ritter visited Britain—a tradition that dated back to the visits by Buffalo Bill and his travelling Wild West show in the 1880s—and television constantly fed our insatiable need for heroes: *The Lone Ranger*, *Hopalong Cassidy*, *Gunsmoke* and many more besides.

Little more than fifty years ago, the final frontier was not space but the wide, rolling ranges of America. The history of the west was still being written. In the early 1950s, Charles Chilton, creator and writer of the hugely popular radio and comic strip series *Riders of the Range*, was made a Deputy Marshal of Tombstone, an appointment reported in great detail in the pages of *Eagle*, the most popular boys' comic of the time. Logic told you that if they still needed marshals, they still had cattle rustlers and stagecoach robberies. It wasn't much of a leap to imagine that marauding bands of Indians were over every hill and gunfights in dusty streets were commonplace. We were utterly convinced.

When Walt Disney released their movie *Davy Crockett, King of the Wild Frontier* in 1955, coonskin hats were on everyone's Christmas list. Playing cowboys and Indians was a part of growing up whether you were born on a mountain top in Tennessee or the badlands of Buckinghamshire.

For over a decade, one of the most popular Western comics published here in Britain was *Cowboy Comics*.

For most of its run, the two main stars were Buck Jones and Kit Carson. Buck Jones was played by actor Charles Gebhart in dozens of movies that lit up cinema screens from the mid-1920s until his death in 1942. Kit Carson was a trapper, guide, soldier and Indian fighter whose life was as full of action as his comic strip counterpart. As a mountain man, Kit was the ideal choice to lead wagon caravans of hopeful migrants heading west; he served with Stephen Kearny's Army of the West, battling Mexicans in New Mexico and California; he fought in the American Civil War and in the Battle of Adobe Walls.

Davy Crockett, like Kit Carson, became an American folk hero; as well as being a frontiersman, Crockett was also a politician although most people remember him as the "King of the Wild Frontier" who "killed him a bear when he was only three" and that he died at the Battle of the Alamo (and the latter only because he was portrayed by John Wayne in the 1960 movie *The Alamo*).

Kansas Kid was a purely fictional character who summed up what *Cowboy Comics* wanted from a hero: a tough and cheerful cowhand, always drifting into trouble.

For children, the Wild West was full of adventure. Rightly or wrongly, we learned about it from movies and television, which meant that there were no grey areas when it came to who was the good guy and who was the bad. White hats would always win over black hats and headdresses. Sitting through boring maths lessons, we imagined ourselves roping steers or camping out under the stars and comic strips like the ones in this book helped feed our imaginations. In our minds we were all "Kings of the Wild Frontier".

Steve Holland

DAVY CROCKETT *and the* Paddleboat Pirates !

HIGH UP AMONG THE SNOW-CLAD PEAKS OF THE OZARK MOUNTAINS, DAVY CROCKETT VIEWED HIS WINTER CATCH OF SKINS AND PELTS WITH SATISFACTION. BOBCAT, MARTIN AND GRIZZLY BEAR HAD FALLEN TO HIS CUNNINGLY PLACED TRAPS — OR TO THE DEADLY AIM OF HIS LONG RIFLE.
NOW THE TIME HAD COME TO TRADE HIS VALUABLE FURS FOR BADLY NEEDED SUPPLIES. QUICKLY HE LOADED HIS BUCKBOARD AND HIT THE TRAIL FOR MELTON'S BLUFF — WHERE THE MISSISSIPPI STEAMBOATS LAY AT ANCHOR, AWAITING CARGO FOR NEW ORLEANS...

THE SUN WAS DIPPING BEHIND THE WESTERN CRAGS WHEN THE SOUND OF GALLOPING HOOFS CAME TO THE FAMOUS HUNTER'S EARS... CRAZED WITH FEAR, A LATHERED SADDLE-HORSE CAREERED WILDLY INTO SIGHT...

A RUNAWAY! GUESS I'D BEST PULL OFF THE TRAIL!

FLINGING HIMSELF FROM THE BUCKBOARD, DAVY SEIZED THE RUNAWAY'S BRIDLE AND BROUGHT THE TERRIFIED HORSE TO A HALT...

WHOA THERE, HOSS! NOT SO FAST, M' BEAUTY!

ARRIVING LIKE AN AVENGING WHIRLWIND, DAVY WENT INTO ACTION WITH THE SPEED OF A STRIKING RATTLESNAKE...

AAAGH!!

ROBBED OF THEIR PREY, THE COWARDLY ROUGHS FLED FOR THE SAFETY OF THE WOODS...

THE CAP'N'S HURT BAD!

THANKS, DAVY! I COULDN'T HAVE HELD OUT MUCH LONGER.

TAKE IT EASY, CAP'N! YOU'RE ABOUT ALL IN!

CAPTAIN MATTHEWS WAS BADLY HURT. AS DAVY DRESSED HIS WOUNDS HE TOLD HIS RESCUER A SORRY TALE OF MISFORTUNE AND DISASTER..

HANK ROGERS IS BEHIND THIS, DAVY! HE'S OUT TO RUIN ME AND GRAB THE RIVER TRADE FOR HIMSELF!

HANK ROGERS, EH? I NEVER DID TAKE TO THAT POISONOUS SKUNK! TELL ME ABOUT HIM, CAP'N.

JOSHUA MATTHEW'S STORY WAS SOON TOLD. HANK ROGERS WAS THE UNSCRUPULOUS CAPTAIN OF A RIVAL MISSISSIPPI PADDLEBOAT. DRIVEN BY INSATIABLE GREED, HE HAD SET OUT TO RUIN CAPTAIN MATHEWS OF THE "LINDY LOU" AND FORCE HIM TO SELL HIS BOAT. NOW, WITH HIS RIVAL BADLY INJURED, IT LOOKED AS IF HE HAD SUCCEEDED.

I SURE HATE TO ADMIT IT, DAVY... BUT I'M FINISHED. HANK ROGERS HAS BEATEN ME. I'M DOWN TO MY LAST DOLLAR!

NOT WHILE I'M AROUND, CAP'N! YOU'VE GOT YOURSELF A NEW PARTNER! MY FURS WILL PAY FOR A REFIT, AND THERE'LL BE ENOUGH LEFT OVER TO HIRE A FIRST-RATE CREW! HANK ROGERS HASN'T WON YET—NOT BY A LONG CHALK!

NEWS OF THE TRANSFORMATION THE ANCIENT PADDLE-BOAT HAD UNDERGONE WITH DAVY'S HELP SPED UP AND DOWN THE RIVER. PASSENGERS FLOCKED TO THE LANDING STAGE TO BE FIRST ABOARD THE ELEGANT STEAMER...

THIS'LL GLADDEN CAP'N MATTHEWS' HEART!

THE MONEY'S ROLLIN' IN FASTER THAN WE CAN COUNT IT, DAVY!

FROM THE WHEEL HOUSE OF HIS OWN CRAFT, HANK ROGERS GLOWERED WITH RAGE AS HE SAW THE VALUABLE RIVER TRADE SLIPPING THROUGH HIS GREEDY FINGERS...

IT'S ALL CROCKETT'S DOIN'! IF HE HADN'T COME ALONG, THAT OLD GOAT MATTHEWS WOULD'VE SOLD OUT WEEKS AGO! BY HEAVEN, I'LL MAKE HIM PAY FOR THIS!

WITH DAVY AT THE HELM, THE "LINDY LOU" STEAMED UP AND DOWN THE RIVER, CARRYING THE CREAM OF THE CARGOES AND THE BULK OF THE TRAVELLERS. CAPTAIN MATTHEWS COULD SCARCELY BELIEVE HIS EYES WHEN HE COUNTED OUT THE GLEAMING PILES OF GOLD AND SILVER DOLLARS DAVY HAD EARNED FOR HIM...

ONLY TWO TRIPS, AND WE'VE MADE A THOUSAND DOLLARS PROFIT! I DON'T KNOW HOW TO THANK YOU, DAVY!

THIS IS ONLY THE BEGINNING, CAP'N! WE'LL SOON BE ABLE TO BUY ANOTHER BOAT. THEN WE'LL DOUBLE OUR TAKIN'S!

WHAT ABOUT HANK ROGERS' CRAFT DAVY? THAT CRITTER WILL SOON BE BROKE AT THE RATE WE'RE STEALIN' HIS TRADE!

AS TRADE BOOMED, DAVY FOUND HIMSELF SHORT OF HANDS. CAPTAIN MATTHEWS, STILL HOBBLING FROM HIS INJURIES, INSISTED ON SAILING WITH HIS PARTNER, AND TWO NEW MEN WERE ADDED TO THE CREW...

I'M NOT MUCH USE YET, DAVY, BUT I CAN AT LEAST CHECK THE CARGOES FOR YOU.

STOW YOUR GEAR IN THE FO'C'SLE, MEN! THE OLD HANDS WILL SHOW YOU YOUR BUNKS!

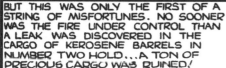

BUT THIS WAS ONLY THE FIRST OF A STRING OF MISFORTUNES. NO SOONER WAS THE FIRE UNDER CONTROL THAN A LEAK WAS DISCOVERED IN THE CARGO OF KEROSENE BARRELS IN NUMBER TWO HOLD...A TON OF PRECIOUS CARGO WAS RUINED!

LOOK, DAVY! THESE BALES ARE SATURATED WITH KEROSENE!

I CAN'T UNDERSTAND IT, JAKE! I CHECKED THOSE BARRELS MYSELF! I'D STAKE MY LIFE THEY WERE SOUND WHEN WE SAILED!

I DON'T LIKE IT, DAVY! THERE'S SOMETHING QUEER GOIN' ON ABOARD THE "LINDY LOU".

KEEP YOUR EYES OPEN JAKE! I'VE GOT A FEELIN' THOSE NEW HANDS ARE BEHIND ALL THIS!

TWO DAYS LATER, THE "LINDY LOU" WAS LOADING FRESH CARGO AT A RIVERSIDE SETTLEMENT, WHEN A ROPE SNAPPED...A MASSIVE BALE OF COTTON CAME HURTLING DOWNWARDS — STRAIGHT TOWARDS CAPTAIN MATTHEWS!

LOOK OUT CAP'N!

DAVY FOLLOWED QUICKLY, SHADOWING THE TWO MEN WITH THE STEALTH OF AN INDIAN...PRESENTLY HE SAW THEM TAP ON THE DOOR OF A LONELY SHACK AT THE EDGE OF THE STRAGGLING TOWNSHIP...

THE DOOR OPENED, AND FOR A FLEETING MOMENT DAVY SAW A BURLY FIGURE SILHOUETTED AGAINST THE LIGHT OF A LANTERN BEFORE THE TWO MEN ENTERED THE CABIN AND THE DOOR CLOSED BEHIND THEM. SEIZING HIS OPPORTUNITY, DAVY MOVED TO THE WINDOW AND LISTENED...

ANGRY VOICES CAME TO HIS KEEN EARS...

SO YOU FAILED, YOU BLUNDERING IDIOTS! THE CAP'N WON'T FORGIVE YOU FOR THIS!

SO I WAS RIGHT! THOSE SKUNKS ARE IN HANK ROGERS' PAY!

WE DID OUR BEST, TOM! BUT THAT GOLDURNED CROCKETT WATCHED US LIKE A HAWK!

BUT DAVY HAD A BETTER PLAN. HE WELCOMED THE CHANCE TO MATCH HIS WITS AGAINST THE VILLAINOUS CAPTAIN ROGERS...

NO, CAP'N! IF ROGERS WANTS A FIGHT— THEN BY HOKEY, HE CAN HAVE ONE! IT'S OUR BIG CHANCE TO SETTLE WITH HIM ONCE AND FOR ALL!

DAVY'S RIGHT, CAP'N! THERE'S NO SENSE IN RUNNING AWAY— LET'S FIGHT IT OUT HERE AN' NOW, I SAY!

RELUCTANTLY, JOSHUA MATTHEWS GAVE IN. NEXT MORNING THE "LINDY LOU" NOSED OUT INTO THE RED RIVER—DEAD ON SCHEDULE. WITH DAVY AT THE HELM, SHE PUFFED AND SNORTED HER WAY TOWARDS THE MOUTH OF THE RIVER...WHERE HANK ROGERS AND HIS MEN LAY IN WAIT....

CROCKETT'S ON HIS WAY, CAP'N! HE DOESN'T SUSPECT ANYTHING!

GOOD! WHEN I STRIKE, HE'LL WONDER WHAT'S HIT HIM!

BARELY WAS THE TREE ABOARD WHEN A CRY FROM HIS LOOK-OUT ANNOUNCED THAT HANK ROGERS' BOAT HAD BEEN SIGHTED. DAVY GRINNED HAPPILY AS HE THOUGHT OF THE SURPRISE HE HAD IN STORE FOR THE MURDEROUS ATTACKERS...

HERE THEY COME, SKIPPER!

LOOK LIVELY, LADS! WE'RE ONLY JUST IN TIME!

EVERY NERVE AND MUSCLE TENSED FOR THE BATTLE AHEAD, DAVY TOOK THE HELM IN HIS CAPABLE HANDS AND SWUNG THE "LINDY LOU" OUT INTO THE MISSISSIPPI UNDER FULL STEAM....

THE FOOLS! THEY'RE SAILIN' RIGHT INTO OUR HANDS!

THE GRINNING SKIPPER CRAMMED ON EVERY OUNCE OF STEAM HE COULD MUSTER AND HEADED THE PROTESTING PADDLEBOAT FOR MELTON'S BLUFF AT FULL SPEED. THE RACE FOR SAFETY WAS ON!

BUT HANK ROGERS' BOAT WAS MORE POWERFUL THAN THE "LINDY LOU". SLOWLY BUT SURELY IT BEGAN TO OVERHAUL THEM...

THEY'RE GAININ' ON US, DAVY! WE DON'T STAND A CHANCE!

IF I DRIVE HER ANY HARDER, I'LL BLOW THE BOILERS, CAP'N! GUESS I'LL HAVE TO PLAY MY LAST CARD!

JUST AS DAVY FELT HE COULD HOLD ON NO LONGER, THE GREAT BAULK OF WOOD SLID INTO POSITION. LASHED AND PINNED TO THE DECK, IT STUCK OUT FROM THE BOWS OF THE "LINDY LOU" LIKE A GIANT SWORDFISH'S SNOUT...

NICE WORK JAKE! LET'S SEE HOW ROGERS LIKES THE LITTLE SURPRISE I'VE PLANNED FOR HIM!

GET UNDER COVER, BOYS! THIS IS WHERE THE FUN BEGINS!

THEN ....

HARD, A-PORT, CAP'N!

...WITH A SICKENING CRUNCH, THE TWO BOATS MET...

AS THE STRICKEN BOAT HEELED DRUNKENLY IN THE SWIRLING WATER, DAVY SEIZED A CUTLASS AND LED HIS CHEERING CREW AS THEY SWARMED ABOARD THE RIVAL CRAFT...

C'MON, BOYS! NOW'S OUR CHANCE!

THAT SURE KNOCKED THE FIGHT OUT OF ROGERS!

The Gun Crew

THE KEGAN GANG, HAVING RAIDED THE BANK IN WICHITA, WERE FLEEING SOUTH PURSUED BY A BIG POSSE. AFTER THREE DAYS, THEY WERE DEEP INTO NEW MEXICO, BUT STILL THE LAW STAYED HARD ON THEIR HEELS...

TWO OF THE POSSE, FLETCHER AND MARTIN LANE WERE DETERMINED TO KEEP ON AFTER THE OUTLAWS. THEY TRADED FOR THE TWO HORSES...

THIS IS CRAZY, MISTER! SUPPOSE YOU DO CATCH UP... WHAT CAN TWO OF YOU DO AGAINST FIVE?

SHERIFF, WHEN WE JOINED UP WITH YOUR POSSE, WE'D ALREADY BEEN HUNTING THEM FELLERS FOR MORE'N A YEAR. WE AIN'T GOING TO STOP NOW!

THE LAWMAN DID NOT KNOW IT, BUT THE LANE BROTHERS HAD A VERY SPECIAL REASON FOR CATCHING UP WITH THE KEGAN GANG!

GOOD LUCK, BOYS!

THEY'LL NEED IT, MISTER... THEY SURE WILL!

MEANWHILE, THE WOUNDED MEMBER OF THE KEGAN GANG COULD KEEP UP WITH THE OTHERS NO LONGER...

SOL... HOLD IT! LOOKS LIKE ALF'S RUN ALL HE CAN...

LEAVE HIM, THEN! HECK, DO YOU WANT US ALL TO STOP AND GET CAUGHT?

SO SPURRING THEIR HORSES, THE OUTLAWS CALLOUSLY LEFT THEIR WOUNDED SIDEKICK TO HIS FATE...

MADRE DE DIOS...

Chapter 2. **Fighting Yankee**

NEXT DAY, WELL AHEAD OF THEIR PURSUERS, THE KEGAN GANG SPLIT UP A FEW MILES NORTH OF KANSAS CITY. SOL KEGAN HAD A PLAN...

THIS IS WHERE WE SPLIT UP. BULL, YOU AND LEX GO GET A JOB WITH ONE OF THE COW OUTFITS. ME AND HEP WILL GO INTO TOWN.

BULL ANDERS AND LEX MARSH HEADED FOR TOWN, AND ON THEIR WAY THEY CAME UPON A COW BRANDING OUTFIT OF THE DOUBLE-D, BOSSED BY THE KANSAS KID.

COUPLE OF STRANGERS! WHAT THEY DOING OUT HERE?

KANSAS DID NOT PARTICULARLY LIKE THE LOOKS OF THE TWO DRIFTERS, BUT HE HAD A BIG ROUND-UP ON HIS HANDS AND WAS SHORT OF MEN. WHEN BULL AND LEX ASKED FOR WORK...

ALL RIGHT... YOU GOT YOURSELVES A JOB. CLIMB DOWN AND EAT.

THANKS, MISTER!

TOWARDS EVENING OF THE SAME DAY, THE LANE BROTHERS SIGHTED THE DOUBLE-D LINE CAMP...

HOW DO WE PICK OUT MEN WE NEVER EVEN SEEN FROM A TOWNFUL OF STRANGERS, FLETCH? BESIDES, I GOT ABOUT TWO DOLLARS LEFT...

WE DON'T, MART. WE GET JOBS WITH A CATTLE OUTFIT UNTIL THE GANG HIT THE BANK. COME ON, LET'S RIDE ON TO THAT CAMP!

KANSAS LIKED THE LOOK OF THE LANE BROTHERS, AND WAS GLAD TO BRING HIS CREW UP TO FULL STRENGTH...

FLETCHER LANE, AND THIS HERE'S MY BROTHER, MARTIN.

GLAD TO HAVE YOU, LANE. I RECKON YOU JUST ABOUT MAKE UP A FULL CREW. C'MON OVER AND MEET THE BOYS!

THE LANES WORKED HARD AND WELL, AND KANSAS KNEW BY THEIR TALK THAT THEY CAME FROM KANSAS...

...FROM LAWRENCE, EH, MART? YOU ANY KIN OF OLD JIM LANE, USED TO RUN THE LAZY T SPREAD UP THERE?

YEAH... WE'RE HIS SONS...

JUST THEN FLETCHER LANE CAME UP. HE OVERHEARD THE CONVERSATION AND INTERRUPTED SHORTLY...

WELL, DURN MY HIDE... IS THAT A FACT! HOW IS OLD JIM?

DEAD, MISTER... AN' WE DON'T WANT TO TALK ABOUT IT!

MART SPREAD HIS OLD UNION ARMY SADDLE BLANKET OVER THE GREY HORSE, CALMLY IGNORING BULL ANDERS' HOARSE BELLOW...

KANSAS SAID TO CUT OUT ANY HORSE I FANCIED, MISTER... AND THAT'S JUST WHAT I'M DOING!

THAT SO, YOU DURN YELLER-LEG? I HAD MY EYE ON THIS CRITTER, SO GET YOURSELF ANOTHER ONE!

MOUTHING CURSES, BULL BEGAN TO DRAG MART'S SADDLE BLANKET OFF THE GREY'S BACK...

I HAD ME THIS BRONC SPOTTED, AN' NO DAMN YANKEE'S GONNA TAKE HIM NOW!

GET YOUR PAWS OFF THAT, MISTER.

HOLD IT!

AS MART'S HANDS WENT UP TO DRAG AWAY THE BLANKET, BULL'S BIG FIST SLAMMED HARD INTO HIS MIDDLE...

AGH...

I'LL SOON KNOCK THE NERVE OUT OF YOU, YANKEE!

BUT BULL WAS IN FOR THE SHOCK OF HIS LIFE. MART RALLIED AND THE SNARLING BULL FELL BACK UNDER A HAIL OF HARD SMASHING BLOWS.

LANE... WHAT IN TARNATION GOES ON HERE?

JUST A FELLER FINDING OUT MART AIN'T SOFT, KANSAS.

THE CREW NOW HAD A NEW RESPECT FOR THE LANE BROTHERS, BUT THEY HAD EARNED THE UNDYING ENMITY OF BIG BULL ANDERS...

HERE, MART. I SPREAD YOUR BEDROLL FOR YOU. SIT DOWN...

LOOK AT THE DAMN YANKEE BRAT... BUT I'LL GET HIM YET. YEAH, I'LL GET HIM, SOONER OR LATER...

NEXT MORNING, SOMEONE HAD TO GO INTO TOWN FOR SUPPLIES AND KANSAS, WANTING TO HELP THE TROUBLE BLOW OVER, SENT BULL AND LEX...

JUST TELL STEVE BOWDEN AT THE STORE TO CHARGE IT TO THE DOUBLE-D. AND DON'T GO HANGING AROUND TOWN. WE NEED THIS STUFF...

YEAH... ALL RIGHT!

ONCE IN TOWN, BULL TOOK THE OPPORTUNITY TO SEE HEP AND SOL...

SAY, WHERE IN TARNATION DID YOU GET THAT BLACKED EYE?

NEVER MIND ABOUT THAT! HOW ABOUT THE JOB?

LEAVING LEX TO LOAD THE WAGON, THE OTHER THREE WENT INTO A SALOON. OVER A GAME OF CARDS, BULL STARTED ASKING QUESTIONS. TOO LOUDLY FOR SOL KEGAN, WHO TURNED AND SNAPPED AT AN OLD-TIMER WHO ENQUIRED IF HE COULD JOIN THEIR GAME...

THAT ROUND-UP'S DAMN' HARD GRAFT, KEGAN! I HOPE YOU TWO...

SORRY, MISTER. THIS IS A PRIVATE GAME. BEAT IT.

SOL THEN TURNED ON BULL, HIS EYES GLARING WITH ANGER...

YOU TALK TOO MUCH, BULL... AND TOO LOUD. SURE, HEP AND I HAVE BEEN BUSY. WE GOT IT FIGURED HOW TO HIT THAT BANK JUST AS SOON'S THE COWMEN DEPOSIT THEIR MONEY!

SOL THEN WENT WITH BULL BACK TO THE WAGON, WHICH WAS NOW LOADED UP AND READY TO GO...

HEP AND ME HAVE EVERYTHING READY. SO YOU JUST GET BACK INTO TOWN AS SOON AS YOU'RE PAID OFF...

SURE WE WILL.

HURRY IT UP, BULL. THAT STOREKEEPER SEEMS TO BE TAKING AN INTEREST IN US...

AS SOL AND HEP WATCHED THEIR PARTNERS DRIVE OUT, SOL VOICED A NAGGING THOUGHT...

THEM LANE BROTHERS BULL WAS TALKING ABOUT... YOU THINK THEY COULD BE KIN OF THE LAWRENCE LANES?

HECK, NO! WHY SHOULD THEY BE? C'MON, LET'S GO AND EAT!

STRANGELY ENOUGH, MART LANE WONDERED ABOUT LEX AND BULL AS THEY DROVE PAST HE AND HIS BROTHER TO THE CAMP...

THERE GOES MARSH AND ANDERS... SAY, FLETCH... DO YOU RECKON THEY COULD BE TWO OF THE KEGAN GANG? THEY GOT HERE JUST BEFORE WE DID!

COULD BE, I GUESS. MIGHT BE AN IDEA TO KEEP AN EYE ON THEM...

Chapter 3.   **Bank Raid**

IN A FEW DAYS THE ROUND-UP WAS COMPLETED, AND THE CATTLE DRIVEN INTO TOWN TO THE STOCKPENS AT THE RAILHEAD...

HERE'S YOUR PAY, BOYS. BUT I SURE COULD USE YOU LANE BROTHERS, IF YOU'RE INTERESTED...

THANKS...BUT WE GOT OTHER WORK ON HAND!

THE LANE BROTHERS TOOK A ROOM AT THE HOTEL, AND WATCHED THE BANK ACROSS THE WAY. WAITING...

I DON'T KNOW, FLETCH... MAYBE WE SHOULD TELL THE SHERIFF...

AND HAVE HIM GET ALL READY FOR THE HOLD UP? NO! WE'LL PLAY IT THE WAY WE SAID.

THEY KNEW THAT THE GANG WOULD STRIKE SOON. MOST OF THE RANCHERS HAD ALREADY DEPOSITED THEIR MONEY, AND THE BANK WAS HEAVY LADEN...

HEY, FLETCH! THERE GOES ANDERS WITH ANOTHER HOMBRE!

HAVING NEVER ACTUALLY SEEN ANY OF THE GANG THEY HAD CHASED OVER SO MANY WEARY MILES, THE LANES DID NOT KNOW THEY WERE LOOKING DOWN AT NONE OTHER THAN SOL KEGAN HIMSELF!

WHERE'S HEP?

HEP'S AT THE LIVERY, SEEING TO THE HORSES. HE KNOWS WHAT TO DO...

FLETCHER LANE WAS STRUCK WITH A SUDDEN HUNCH.

MART, I GUESS MAYBE YOU WERE RIGHT ABOUT ANDERS AND MARSH. THIS COULD BE IT.

WANT ME TO GO GET THE HORSES READY? JUST IN CASE...

YEAH!

AS MART FELL TO HIS KNEES BESIDE THE OLD MAN, HEP STEPPED UP QUICKLY AND SWUNG DOWN THE BARREL OF HIS GUN...

MISTER EVANS! YOU...AARGH!

WHEN, A FEW MINUTES LATER, SOL KEGAN CAME TO MAKE A LAST MINUTE CHECK WITH HEP, THE SIGHT OF MART GAVE HIM A SUDDEN IDEA.

GET THEM PANTS OFF HIM. BULL, YOU SADDLE THEIR HORSES!

SOL THEN MADE BULL PUT ON MART'S BRITCHES...

HUSTLE, DURN IT. IT'S TIME WE WAS AT THE BANK!

SOL... SOMEONE COMING!

WHEN THE KANSAS KID HEARD OF THE RAID IT WAS NIGHTFALL, AND THE POSSE WAS LONG GONE WHEN HE RODE INTO TOWN. HE FOUND OLD BEN PARKS, THE DEPUTY, IN CHARGE OF THE JAIL...

HOWDY, KANSAS! IF YOU'VE COME TO JOIN THE POSSE, YOU'RE TOO LATE!

HOWDY, BEN. I'VE COME TO SEE THE TWO BOYS YOU'VE GOT LOCKED UP...

KANSAS LISTENED TO THE BROTHERS' STORY AND BELIEVED THEM. BUT HE WAS THE ONLY ONE WHO DID!

TARNATION, BEN. I KNOW THESE BOYS ARE TELLING THE TRUTH!

MAYBE, KANSAS. BUT I CAN'T LET THEM GO, I JUST CAN'T.

BUT FINALLY, KANSAS MANAGED TO PERSUADE OLD BEN TO RELEASE JUST ONE OF THE BROTHERS, KEEPING FLETCHER AS A "HOSTAGE".

TAKE IT EASY, FLETCH. WE'LL BE BACK!

YOU BETTER BE, SON. YOU JUST BETTER BE, THAT'S ALL

LET'S GO, MART.

Chapter 4.   Outlaw Round-Up

HAVING BEEN TOLD WHICH WAY THE POSSE HAD HEADED, KANSAS LED MART OVER A MOUNTAIN SHORT-CUT DANGEROUS EVEN BY FULL DAYLIGHT...

WE'LL PICK UP THEIR TRAIL AT THE END OF THE PASS!

TWO HOURS LATER, THEY CAME UP ON THE POSSE CAMPED BY A STREAM IN THE MOONLIGHT...

HOWDY, KANSAS! WHO'S THAT YOU GOT WITH YOU? THERE'S SOME GRAIN FOR YOUR HORSES IN THE NOSEBAGS.

WHEN MART LANE HEARD THAT THE POSSE WAS FEEDING TO THEIR HORSES GRAIN "ABANDONED" BY THE ROBBERS, HE SPRANG FORWARD...

DON'T FEED THAT GRAIN!

WHAT...SAY! THAT'S THAT LANE FELLER!

HOLD IT, SHERIFF! THAT GOES FOR ALL OF YOU!

EXPLANATIONS FOLLOWED FAST, AND KANSAS WON THE SHERIFF OVER WHEN MART TOLD ABOUT THE OUTLAWS' TRICK OF DROPPING POISONED GRAIN...

SEE THEM LITTLE SEEDS? THAT'S BRACKWEED. GUARANTEED TO PUT ANY HORSE OUT OF ACTION FOR WELL NIGH A FULL DAY!

BY GOLLY, HE'S RIGHT! LOOK AT MY HORSE...HE'S DOWN!

THE OUTLAWS HAD OUTSMARTED THE POSSE... BUT THEY STILL HAD TO RECKON WITH MART LANE AND THE KANSAS KID. AFTER A BRIEF REST...

MAYBE I SHOULD TAKE LANE'S HORSE, KANSAS...

NO, SHERIFF. PLAY THIS MY WAY, AND I PROMISE YOU WE WON'T COME BACK WITHOUT THE BANK'S MONEY

AS THEY RODE, MART TOLD KANSAS HOW HIS PARENTS HAD BEEN KILLED AND THEIR HOME BURNED BY QUANTRILL'S RAIDERS IN THE TERRIBLE ATTACK ON LAWRENCE, AND HOW HE AND HIS BROTHER HAD HUNTED KEGAN AND THORP FOR THEIR PART IN THE HORRIBLE RAID...

YOU THINK KEGAN AND THORP FIRED YOUR HOME?

SURE OF IT! PA LIVED LONG ENOUGH TO NAME THE SKUNKS!

SMALL WONDER THAT THE LANE BROTHERS HAD STUCK SO HARD AND SO LONG ON THE TRAIL OF KEGAN'S GANG!

HEY, SOL! TWO RIDERS ABOUT FIVE MILES BACK!

TARNATION! HEP YOU SURE YOU DOCTORED THAT GRAIN FOOD? WE'D BETTER MOVE ON!

BUT SOL HAD RECKONED WITHOUT THE KEEN EYES OF KANSAS, WHO SPOTTED THE MARKS ON THE TRAIL AHEAD WHERE SOMEONE HAD LEFT IT. SUDDENLY, HE SHOUTED A WARNING... AND A SHOT RANG OUT... FROM ABOVE...

LOOK OUT!

THE KID'S QUICK SHOUT HAD MADE BULL FIRE HASTILY, AND THE SHOT STRUCK MART'S HORSE. AS THE ANIMAL FELL, KANSAS DRAGGED MART CLEAR...

THEY'RE UP THERE... BEHIND THOSE BOULDERS...

SECURE BEHIND THEIR COVER, BULL AND LEX WAITED TO PICK OFF THEIR PREY SHOULD EITHER ONE MAKE THE SLIGHTEST MOVE...

DURN IT, BULL! YOU SHOT TOO QUICK!

SO WHAT? WE GOT THEM, AIN'T WE? SOON'S ONE MAKES A MOVE HE'S A DEAD MAN.

BUT KANSAS HAD OTHER IDEAS.

BEST SAVE YOUR LEAD KANSAS. THEY GOT TOO MUCH COVER!

I'M NOT SHOOTING AT THEM, MART. THAT TREE UP THERE IS MY TARGET!

BULL BROKE COVER IN A PLUNGING RUSH, THROWING LEAD AT MART AND KANSAS AS FAST AS HE COULD THUMB THE HAMMER...

BUT, KANSAS, SLUGS KICKING UP SPITEFUL DUST FLURRIES ALL AROUND HIM, STOOD UP CALMLY AND DROPPED BULL WITH A SINGLE SHOT...

AS KANSAS MOUNTED UP AND SET OUT TO CATCH THE FLEEING HORSES, MART WENT TO THE GROANING LEX, PINNED UNDER THE FALLEN TREE...

AAARGH... GET ME OUT... GET ME OUT!

DON'T WORRY, MISTER... YOU AIN'T GOING TO DIE... YET!

ONLY SLIGHTLY WORRIED BY THE PERSISTANT PAIR ON THEIR HEELS, SOL'S CUNNING BRAIN WORKED FAST WHEN THEY MET UP WITH A CHUCK-WAGON...

BETTER WATCH HOW YOU RIDE IF YOU'RE HEADED THROUGH THE CANYON, MISTER. WE GOT A HERD COMIN' THROUGH, AN' THE BOYS'RE PUSHING 'EM MIGHTY HARD...

THANKS...

AS THEY PRESSED ON INTO THE CANYON, HEP'S BACKWARD GLANCES BECAME WORRIED. BUT SOL ONLY GRINNED...

THEY'RE CLOSIN' ON US, SOL THEY'RE CLOSIN' FAST!

GOOD... THAT'S JUST FINE! LET THEM GET WELL INTO THE CANYON!

HEP SCRAMBLED ON TO HIS TERRIFIED HORSE AND PUT THE ANIMAL AT THE SLOPE ... TOO LATE. THE BELLOWING HERD WAS ON HIM ...

AAARGH...

KANSAS HEARD THE SHOTS BOOMING IN THE CANYON, AND THE SUDDEN BELLOWING OF THE FEAR-CRAZED STEERS...

THEY MUST HAVE STAMPEDED THAT HERD. LET'S GO!

AS KANSAS AND MART TURNED THEIR HORSES, THE HERD CAME CHARGING THROUGH THE CANYON.

FASTER, MART... FASTER! FALL OFF, AND YOU'LL BE JUST A SMEAR ON THE GROUND!

AN HOUR LATER, THE HERD HALTED. ACHING ALL OVER AND HALF-CHOKED WITH DUST, THE TWO OF THEM RECEIVED THE ADMIRING THANKS OF THE TRAIL BOSS...

THE NAME'S GIL COOMBS, MISTER...AN' I'M TRULY PROUD TO MEET YOU BOYS! THAT SURE WAS A GREAT JOB YOU DONE THERE...

THE HERD NOW UNDER CONTROL AGAIN, GIL WENT WITH KANSAS AND MART BACK DOWN THE CANYON TO LOOK FOR SIGN. THEY FOUND HEP BADLY HURT...

THAT ONE OF YOUR MEN, GIL?

DON'T LOOK LIKE ONE... NOPE...

SIGHT OF HEP BROUGHT BACK TO MART A RUSH OF MEMORIES OF HIS MURDERED FOLKS... HE DISMOUNTED WITH A SOB OF RAGE, CLAWING AT HIS HOLSTERED GUN...

IT'S KEGAN, IT MUST BE!

HOLD IT, MART! THAT'S NOT THE WAY!

NO...NO! I'M NOT KEGAN!

Chapter 5. **Last Of The Gang**

KANSAS AND MART STAYED ON JUST LONG ENOUGH TO SNATCH A QUICK HOT MEAL BEFORE TAKING UP SOL KEGAN'S TRAIL.

SURE WAS GOOD, OLD TIMER, BUT THANKS, NO MORE. WE GOT TO BE RIDING!

ELI, GET THEM A SACK OF PROVISIONS. HUSTLE, NOW!

DEEPLY GRATEFUL FOR WHAT THEY HAD DONE FOR HIM AND HIS HERD, THE TRAIL BOSS GAVE MART A FRESH HORSE, AND KANSAS HIS SOLEMN WORD...

DON'T WORRY ABOUT A THING, KANSAS! I'LL GET THAT GALOOT AN' THIS HERE MONEY INTO TOWN, EVEN IF I HAVE TO LEAVE MY HERD BEHIND TO DO IT!

THE STAMPEDE OVER, SOL CALLOUSLY ABANDONED HIS INJURED PARTNER AND WITH HALF THE MONEY LEFT, PRESSED ON FOR THE BORDER...

REACHING A TRADING POST RUN BY A HALF-BREED APACHE, SOL RECOGNISED ONE OF HIS OWN KIND.

THEM BOYS OUT THERE...THEY IN THE MARKET FOR WORK? WELL PAID WORK?

THEY DO WHAT I TELL THEM, SOMETHING YOU WANT DONE?

SOL HAD PLENTY OF MONEY AND WAS TAKING NO CHANCES. HE PAID THE HALF-BREED TO STOP ANYONE WHO MIGHT COME AFTER HIM...

MAYBE NOBODY WILL COME...IN WHICH CASE YOU GOT A HUNDRED BUCKS FOR NOTHIN'. BUT IF SOMEBODY DOES COME...

DON'T WORRY. THEY NEVER REACH THE RIO GRANDE...

RIO GRANDE

WHEN SOL HAD GONE, THE HALF-BREED TRADER GRUNTED INSTRUCTIONS TO THE THREE APACHE BUCKS...

SOON, MAYBE TWO MEN COME. THEY MUST NOT REACH THE RIVER.

KANSAS APPROACHED THE TRADING POST WARILY, AT DUSK. HE KNEW THE HALF-BREED, AND HIS SHADY REPUTATION...

STAY HERE AN' COVER ME, MART. I WOULDN'T TRUST THE BREED WHO RUNS THIS PLACE FURTHER THAN I CAN THROW HIM!

KANSAS DID NOT EXPECT THE TRUTH... AND HE DID NOT GET IT. BUT HIS QUICK EYES PICKED OUT THE SIGNS OF SOL'S VISIT...

LOOK, I TOLD YOU, ALREADY! NOBODY BEEN HERE ALL DAY! NOW, YOU WANT TO BUY SOMETHIN'? OTHERWISE, I'M BUSY...

ALL RIGHT, BRADY... BUT WATCH IT, MISTER! ONE DAY YOU'LL GO JUST THAT LITTLE BIT TOO FAR!

KANSAS KNEW BY THE TWO WHISKY GLASSES, AND THE MARKS OF A SINGLE SHOD HORSE, THAT THE HALF BREED WAS LYING...

WELL, KANSAS!

KEGAN WAS THERE, ALL RIGHT, BUT BRADY LIED ABOUT IT... I WONDER WHY?

THEY PRESSED ON TO THE RIO GRANDE, BUT WHEN THEY SIGHTED THE RIVER AT DUSK, SOL KEGAN HAD ALREADY CROSSED OVER INTO MEXIO.

THERE SHE IS, MART, ON THE OTHER SIDE IS OLD MEXICO...

I'VE CHASED KEGAN ALL THE WAY FROM KANSAS, AN' I SURE AIN'T GOIN' TO LET A BORDER STOP ME NOW!

KANSAS DECIDED TO CAMP ON THIS SIDE OF THE RIVER, CROSSING OVER AFTER KEGAN IN THE MORNING. BUT JUST BEFORE DAWN, THREE APACHES CREPT UP ON THEIR CAMP...

THE APACHE SHAFTS THUDDED INTO THE BLANKET-WRAPPED TARGETS, THEN THEY RUSHED DOWN THE SLOPE TO MAKE THEIR FINAL THRUSTS...

BUT THIS WAS NO ORDINARY RIDER THE APACHES HAD BEEN SENT TO DEAL WITH... THIS WAS THE KANSAS KID. HE AND MART WERE WAITING FOR THE ATTACK!

I THOUGHT MAYBE WE'D BE GETTIN' A VISIT!

YAAARRGH!

THE APACHES' SNARLS OF TRIUMPH TURNED TO YELLS OF ALARM... THEN TO GRUNTS OF AGONY AS THE TWO 'VICTIMS' TURNED THE TABLES.

AAARRGH...

AT THE BAR, KANSAS SPOKE TO THE CANTINA OWNER.

GRACIAS, PATRON. THE RICH GRINGO. HE IS YOUR GUEST?

SUCH QUESTIONS COST MONEY, HOMBRE!

A GOLD PIECE CHANGED HANDS ACROSS THE BAR TOP, AND KANSAS GOT THE NUMBER OF KEGAN'S ROOM.

I'LL GO TAKE A LOOK AT HIS ROOM. REMEMBER, MART... DON'T START ANYTHING! IF HE FOLLOWS ME, LET HIM!

OKAY, KANSAS... BUT I DON'T LIKE IT!

KANSAS MOUNTED THE STAIRS UN-NOTICED, AND SLIPPED INTO KEGAN'S ROOM. BELOW, MART WATCHED...

SO FAR, SO GOOD!

BUT NO SOONER WAS KANSAS INSIDE THE ROOM, THAN THE BARKEEP CROSSED TO KEGAN'S TABLE WITH A FRESH BOTTLE.

PERHAPS YOU SHOULD SEE THAT ALL IS WELL IN YOUR ROOM, SENOR...

WHAT... TARNATION!

ONCE IN THE ROOM, KANSAS GOT TO WORK... FAST. HE TORE THE PLACE APART, UNTIL...

THE STOLEN MONEY. FOUND IT, BY HOKEY!

MART WATCHED KEGAN FOLLOW KANSAS UP BUT, AS THE KID HAD TOLD HIM, HE DID NOTHING TO INTERVENE. . . .

HOLD IT RIGHT THERE, MISTER.

KANSAS MOVED WITH THE SPEED OF A STRIKING RATTLER. AS HE WHIRLED, HE FLUNG THE PILLOW WITH ALL HIS MIGHT, AND SOL'S SHOT BLASTED WILD. . . .

AAAGH. . .

AS KEGAN'S NEW FRIENDS SCRAMBLED TO HELP HIM, MART'S VOICE RANG OUT...

HOLD IT! I'LL KILL THE FIRST MAN TO MAKE A MOVE!

GOOD FOR YOU, MART! I'LL BE RIGHT DOWN!

THE RABBLE LOOKED INTO THE STEELY EYES OF THE TWO DETERMINED MEN, AND DECIDED THAT THEY HAD NOT KNOWN KEGAN LONG ENOUGH TO DIE FOR HIM.

GET HIM OUTSIDE, AND ON TO HIS HORSE, MART, I'LL LEAVE THIS MOB SOMETHING TO FIGHT OVER...

AS MART WAS LOADING THE DAZED AND BATTERED KEGAN ON TO HIS HORSE, KANSAS FLUNG A HANDFUL OF GOLD DOWN ONTO THE CANTINA FLOOR!

THEY'RE ALL YOURS, AMIGOS! ADIOS!

AND AS THE MEXICANS SCRAMBLED FOR THE COINS, KANSAS JOINED MART, WAITING AND READY TO RIDE.

THE OLD MEXICAN WAS WAITING AT THE EDGE OF TOWN WITH THEIR HORSES AS THE MANHUNTERS HUSTLED UP WITH THEIR PRISONER...

GOLDURN IT, KANSAS! SMARTEST PIECE OF WORK I EVER SAW...

SAVE IT, MART! WE GOT NO TIME TO LOSE!

WITH THE LANE BROTHERS REUNITED, AND KEGAN IN JAIL AWAITING HIS JUST DESERTS, KANSAS' JOB WAS DONE...

THIS BANK REWARD... KANSAS... IT'S RIGHTLY YOURS. WE CAN'T TAKE IT... YOU DONE ENOUGH FOR US ALREADY.

SURE YOU CAN TAKE IT! BE A GOOD START FOR YOU BACK HOME. ADIOS, BOYS... AND GOOD LUCK.

KANSAS DID NOT STOP TO ARGUE. THERE WAS WORK WAITING AT THE DOUBLE-D, AND HE HAD BEEN TOO LONG AWAY FROM IT.

THERE GOES A REAL BIG MAN, FLETCH...

YOU CAN SAY THAT AGAIN, BOY. YOU SURE CAN!

KIT CARSON *and the*
MAN WHO HATED REDSKINS

Chapter 1. THE CHIEF'S REVENGE

ON A FINE SEPTEMBER MORNING, A CAVALRY PATROL ARRIVED BACK AT FORT SMITH, ON THE ARKANSAS RIVER, WITH A YOUNG REDSKIN PRISONER. WHEN KIT CARSON, THE FAMOUS SCOUT, RECOGNISED THE PRISONER, HE FELT A SHOCK OF ASTONISHMENT — *AND DISMAY!*

IT'S YOUNG SWIFT ARROW, SON OF CHIEF MANY CLOUDS OF THE CHEROKEES!

BUT BACK IN FORT SMITH, KIT CARSON HAD FORSEEN THE DANGER TO YOUNG DEXTER...

I KNOW HOW MANY CLOUDS' MIND WORKS. HE'LL STRIKE BACK THROUGH THE COLONEL'S SON!

AND NOW THE FAMOUS SCOUT WAS RIDING OUT TO PREVENT A TRAGEDY.

KIT KNEW THE AREA IN WHICH THE PATROL WAS WORKING AND, TWO DAYS LATER, HE CAME UPON THEIR TRACKS...

FRESH TRACKS! THEY CAN'T BE MORE THAN A FEW MILES AWAY...

BEFORE SUNDOWN, THE SCOUT CAME UP WITH THE PATROL, AND WARNED LIEUTENANT DEXTER OF HIS DANGER...

...SO IF YOU TAKE MY ADVICE, LIEUTENANT, YOU'LL RETURN TO THE FORT RIGHT AWAY.

BUT AT THAT VERY MOMENT THE PATROL WAS BEING WATCHED BY EAGLE-KEEN EYES...

KIT RODE AWAY, BUT HE DID NOT GO BEYOND SIGHT OF THE PATROL...

THE PATROL DISAPPEARED IN A SUDDEN DIP, AND ALMOST AT ONCE THERE WAS AN OUTBURST OF RIFLE FIRE ...

TARNATION!

IN A FLASH, KIT SAW THAT THE PATROL HAD RIDDEN INTO A TRAP, FOR THE SIDES OF THE VALLEY WERE ALIVE WITH CHEROKEES...

BY CRACKY, THIS IS A FULL STRENGTH WAR-PARTY! MANY CLOUDS REALLY MEANS BUSINESS!

NEXT MOMENT, A BULLET RIPPED ACROSS KIT'S LEFT SHOULDER AND KNOCKED HIM FROM THE SADDLE...

...TO SMACK HIS HEAD AGAINST THE GROUND WITH STUNNING FORCE!

THE SCOUT WAS LYING UNCONSCIOUS WHEN, QUICKLY, MANY CLOUDS AND FOUR PICKED WARRIORS SWOOPED ON THE LIEUTENANT...

THE RESOLUTE BAND OF CHEROKEES MADE SURE OF THEIR QUARRY...

LEAVING THEIR COMPANIONS TO DEAL WITH THE REST OF THE PATROL, THE CHIEF AND HIS BRAVES RODE OFF WITH THEIR CAPTIVE...

WHEN KIT CAME TO, THE SERGEANT TOLD HIM THE GRIM TRUTH...

...AND THEY GRABBED THE LOOTENANT BEFORE I COULD DO ANYTHING, AND TOOK HIM OFF!

WELL, DO WHAT I SAY AND I'LL GET YOU OUT OF HERE.

ONCE BACK AT THE FORT, KIT REPORTED TO THE COLONEL, AND AS HE LISTENED, A LOOK OF HORROR CAME INTO DEXTER'S EYES...

MY SON? IN REDSKIN HANDS?

YES, SIR. AND THIS MEANS THAT NOW, MORE THAN EVER, YOU MUST NOT HARM A HAIR OF SWIFT ARROW'S HEAD. IF YOU DO—THEN HEAVEN HELP THE LIEUTENANT!

THE COLONEL SEEMED STUNNED...

I'VE BEEN FIGHTING REDSKINS ALL MY LIFE, CARSON— AND THIS IS ONE TIME I DON'T KNOW WHAT TO DO!

GIVE ME A FEW DAYS TO GET MY STRENGTH BACK, SIR, AND I'LL GO TO MANY CLOUDS AND MAKE A BARGAIN WITH HIM. HIS SON, UNHARMED—FOR YOUR SON, UNHARMED!

THE COLONEL AGREED, BUT EIGHT DAYS LATER, THE TRADER, JED STRAWN, ARRIVED AT THE FORT WITH HIS RIVERBOAT...

KIT SAW THE LOOK OF DEMENTED FURY THAT CAME INTO THE COLONEL'S FACE, AND STEPPED FORWARD...

STRAWN IS LYING, SIR! THE CHEROKEES NEVER TORTURE THEIR PRISONERS AT THE STAKE! HE IS JUST TRYING TO MAKE TROUBLE...

STRAWN APPEALED TO HIS PARTNERS.

BOYS, AIN'T I TELLING THE TRUTH?

YOU SURE ARE, JED. I'D LIKE TO SAY YOU WASN'T, BUT WE ALL SEEN HIM.

AIN'T NO OTHER LIEUTENANT IN THIS NECK OF THE WOODS WITH HAIR AS RED AS HIS.

LEAVING THE HORSES IN THE SHADOWS, KIT CRAWLED UP BEHIND THE TENT AND SLIT THE CANVAS...

LUCKY THERE'S NO MOON...

SOON KIT WAS INSIDE THE TENT, WHISPERING TO THE YOUNG REDSKIN AS HE CUT HIS BONDS...

...AND YOUR PONY IS WAITING A FEW PACES BEHIND THE TENT TETHERED TO A PICKET STAKE. I WILL GET THE GUARD TO OPEN THE GATES, BUT WAIT UNTIL I GIVE AN OWL'S HOOT THEN RIDE HARD!

THEN KIT RODE TOWARDS THE FORT GATE...

HALT! WHO GOES THERE?

CARSON!

THE SENTRY OPENED THE GATE FOR THE FAMOUS SCOUT WITHOUT QUESTION...

THIS IS A HECK OF A TIME FOR YOU TO SET OUT, KIT.

YOU EVER KNOW AN ARMY SCOUT THAT KEPT REGULAR HOURS?

AS SOON AS THE GATE WAS OPEN, KIT GAVE THE HOOT-OWL SIGNAL. ALMOST AT ONCE, THERE WAS THE SOUND OF GALLOPING HOOVES...

HEY! WHAT—

AS ONE OF THE SENTRIES RAISED HIS CARBINE TO SHOOT THE ESCAPING REDSKIN, KIT SWUNG HIS HORSE INTO HIM, KNOCKING HIM OFF BALANCE, AND THE SOLDIER FIRED HARMLESSLY INTO THE AIR. DISTRACTED BY THIS, THE OTHER SENTRY'S SHOT WENT WIDE OF ITS TARGET!

REALISING KIT WAS HELPING THE INDIAN TO ESCAPE, ONE OF THE SENTRIES CALLED FOR HELP. AND NO SOONER HAD THE SCOUT CLOSED THE FORT GATE...AND MET THE OTHER SENTRY WITH A CRASHING BLOW TO THE JAW...THAN TROOPERS CAME RUNNING TO THEIR COMRADES' AID...

SEIZE CARSON! HE HELPED THE INJUN GET AWAY!

IN THE THREE DAYS LEFT TO HIM, KIT DEVISED A PLAN TO ESCAPE. AS HE WOULD BE TAKEN OUTSIDE THE FORT TO BE SHOT, HIS BEST CHANCE WOULD COME AT THE LAST MOMENT...

WHEN THEY TIE MY HANDS AGAIN AFTER THIS MEAL, I MUST TRY TO WORK MY BONDS LOOSE...

FOR HOURS KIT STRAINED ON THE CORDS BINDING HIS WRISTS, UNTIL AT LAST, THEY HAD STRETCHED SUFFICIENTLY FOR HIM TO BE ABLE TO RELEASE HIS HANDS AT THE LAST VITAL MOMENT...

WHEN THE DREAD DAWN CAME AT LAST, AND AS KIT WAS MARCHED WITH THE FIRING SQUAD TOWARDS THE FORT GATE, THUNDER SENSED THAT HIS MASTER WAS IN TROUBLE. THE GREAT HORSE BECAME RESTLESS AND WITH A LOUD WHINNY, TUGGED ON THE PICKET ROPE.

THE FORT GATE WAS FLUNG OPEN AND AS KIT AND HIS ESCORT MARCHED THROUGH, HE GAVE THE LONG, PIERCING WHISTLE THAT THUNDER KNEW SO WELL...

THAT WHISTLE WAS ALL THUNDER NEEDED...

THE PICKET ROPE SNAPPED LIKE THREAD... AND THE GIANT HORSE WAS FREE!

NEXT MOMENT THE WHITE STALLION THUNDERED THROUGH THE GROUP OF SOLDIERS AND, IN A FLASH, KIT HAD HIS HANDS FREE AND WAS LEAPING ON TO HIS HORSE'S BACK...

GOOD WORK, BOY! NOW LET'S GET OUT OF HERE...FAST!

HE'S ESCAPING... QUICK...SHOOT HIM!

EVENTUALLY, THE NEWS OF KIT CARSON'S ESCAPE REACHED STRAWN...

I DON'T LIKE THIS! CARSON IS A GREAT MAN FOR PACIFYING INJUNS. WE GOT TO THINK OF SOMETHING, BOYS!

BY THAT EVENING, KIT HAD REACHED THE BIG DAM THAT THE CHEROKEES HAD BUILT TO KEEP THE RIVER FROM FLOODING THEIR VALLEY,

THE RIVER IS SURE FLOODED. THE HIGHEST I'VE EVER SEEN IT!

BUT INSTEAD OF FLEEING IMMEDIATELY, KIT SURPRISED THE CHEROKEES BY SENDING HIS STALLION LEAPING FORWARD AT THE LAST MOMENT, JUST WHEN THEY WERE ALMOST UPON HIM AND BEFORE THEY COULD CHECK THEIR MOUNTS.

THE PALEFACE IS MAD! HE IS HEADING FOR OUR CAMP!

YES, WE HAVE HIM AT OUR MERCY NOW, BIG BULL!

THEY FETCHED YOUNG DEXTER, WHO STARED IN AMAZEMENT WHEN HE SAW KIT....

CARSON! DID THEY CAPTURE YOU, TOO?

LIEUTENANT, I AM GOING TO FIGHT FOR BOTH OF US...

KIT EXPLAINED THE SITUATION....

THEN, IN A CLEARING, A TOMAHAWK WAS SUNK INTO A TREE-STUMP...

AT MY SIGNAL YOU LEAP FOR THE TOMAHAWK.

AS THEY WRESTLED TOGETHER, SEARING AGONY WENT THROUGH KIT'S LEFT SHOULDER, AND BIG BULL BROKE FREE. IN A FLASH KIT GRABBED THE BIG BRAVE'S LEFT WRIST AND FLUNG HIMSELF BACKWARDS...

USING HIS OUT-THRUST FOOT AS A LEVER, KIT THREW BIG BULL CLEAN OVER HIS HEAD...

UGG-HH!

TO THE ASTONISHMENT OF THE ONLOOKERS, THE FAMOUS SCOUT HELPED THE SHAKEN BIG BULL TO HIS FEET...

IS IT PEACE BETWEEN US, BIG BULL?

WAUGH! YOU ARE INDEED A GREAT WARRIOR, LONG-HAIR! YES, IT IS PEACE!

SOME OF THE BRAVES SHOUTED ANGRILY, DISAPPOINTED AT THE WAY THE CONTEST HAD GONE, BUT THE CHIEF KEPT HIS BARGAIN...

MANY CLOUDS ALWAYS KEEPS HIS WORD, RED HAIR, YOU ARE FREE TO GO.

LOOKING AT DEXTER, KIT REALISED THAT THE YOUNG LIEUTENANT WAS THE KEY TO PEACE.

YOU MUST GET BACK TO FORT SMITH AS SOON AS YOU'RE FIT, LIEUTENANT, AS LONG AS YOUR FATHER THINKS THE REDSKINS HAVE KILLED YOU, HE IS LIABLE TO DO SOMETHING THAT WILL START A WAR.

CRAZED WITH HATRED AND THE IMAGINED LOSS OF HIS SON, THE COLONEL AGREED TO LET STRAWN HAVE HALF THE POWDER FROM THE FORT'S MAGAZINE...

LATER, AS THE *SOUTHERN BELLE* HEADED UPRIVER WITH ITS DANGEROUS CARGO...

I DON'T LIKE BLOWIN' UP THE OLD *BELLE*, EVEN IF SHE AIN'T MUCH GOOD!

WHAT ARE YOU WORRYIN' ABOUT, CAP'N? SHE'S INSURED, AND WE'LL MAKE MONEY ON IT!

THEN, BACK AT FORT SMITH...

IT'S KIT CARSON! COMIN' BACK OF HIS OWN ACCORD! TELL THE COLONEL!

THE RELIEF ON THE COLONEL'S FACE WAS SOON SUCCEEDED BY ONE OF DISMAY AS HE REALISED WHAT HE HAD DONE.

CARSON, STRAWN IS MAKING FOR THE DAM AT THIS VERY MOMENT, TO BREACH IT!

KIT'S HEART WENT COLD AS THE COLONEL EXPLAINED THE SCHEME, FOR THIS COULD RUIN ALL HIS HOPES FOR PEACE...

KIT POINTED OUT THAT LIEUTENANT DEXTER WOULD BE AT THE RIVER END OF THE VALLEY WHEN THE DAM WENT, AND IN TERRIBLE PERIL...

SOMEONE HAS TO STOP STRAWN—AND THUNDER IS THE FASTEST HORSE ON THE POST! IT'S NO USE SENDING A SQUADRON AFTER HIM, FOR WE CAN'T TAKE CHANCES!

CARSON IS NO LONGER UNDER ARREST! GIVE HIM ALL THE HELP HE NEEDS! I'LL GIVE YOU WRITTEN ORDERS FOR STRAWN, KIT!

Chapter 4. TREACHERY AFLOAT
AN HOUR LATER, THE FAMOUS SCOUT WAS PICKING HIS DANGEROUS WAY THROUGH SNAKE-INFESTED SWAMPS...
WATCH IT, THUNDER! ONE FALSE STEP IN THIS SWAMP, AND NEITHER OF US WILL BE SEEN AGAIN!

BUT THE TREACHEROUS SWAMP WAS NOT THE ONLY PERIL THEY HAD TO FACE...

AFTER A NIGHTMARE RIDE, KIT CAME OUT AT THE UPRIVER END OF THE DAM...

NO SIGN OF STRAWN'S BOAT, WHICH MEANS THAT I'VE GOT AHEAD OF IT.   SO I'LL GO DOWNRIVER TO MEET HIM, AND KEEP TO THE BANK ALL THE WAY...

NIGHT HAD FALLEN BY THE TIME KIT SAW.
BY THE LIGHT OF A CRESCENT MOON, THE
OLD RIVERBOAT SLOWLY THRESHING ITS
WAY UPSTREAM AGAINST THE FLOOD.

AS THE BOAT DREW CLOSER, KIT
HAILED HER, BUT WHEN HIS
SHOUTS WERE NOT HEARD HE
RAISED HIS RIFLE...

A BULLET
OR TWO ACROSS
HER BOWS WILL
STOP HER!

WHEN HE REACHED A POINT WELL AHEAD OF THE BOAT, KIT GOT READY TO SWIM...

YOU STAY HERE, THUNDER. IT SHOULDN'T TAKE ME LONG.

SOON KIT WAS IN THE WATER, STRIKING OUT STRONGLY TO MEET THE BOAT...

LEAVING KIT IN THE WHEELHOUSE, STRAWN WENT DOWN INTO THE CABIN DIRECTLY BELOW AND SHOWED THE COLONEL'S LETTER TO HIS PARTNERS...

... SO YOU WILL OBEY THE INSTRUCTIONS CARSON WILL GIVE YOU. ON NO ACCOUNT MUST THE DAM BE DAMAGED...

THEY MUST BE ON TO US NOW— THE COLONEL'S FOUND OUT WE WERE LYIN' ABOUT HIS SON!

SO WHAT ? LYIN' AIN'T NO CRIME— OR WE CAN SAY IT WAS A MISTAKE. WHAT'S WORSE IS THAT EVERYTHIN' IS GOING TO BE PEACEFUL NOW, AND THERE WON'T BE AN INDIAN WAR! ...UNLESS...

WELL, WHAT ARE YOU GOIN' TO DO, JED?

WE GET RID OF CARSON, BLOW THE DAM AS PLANNED, AND PRETEND TO THE COLONEL AFTERWARDS THAT CARSON NEVER REACHED US, WITH THE MESSAGE!

WHILE FLORY, KNIFE IN HAND, CONCEALED HIMSELF IN THE SHADOWS AT THE FOOT OF THE STAIRS, STRAWN CALLED THE SCOUT WAITING IN THE WHEELHOUSE ABOVE...

WILL YOU COME DOWN HERE, CARSON? WE AIN'T TOO GOOD AT READIN', AND WE DON'T SAVVY ALL OF THIS...

SUSPECTING TREACHERY, KIT MOVED CAUTIOUSLY DOWNSTAIRS, EVERY MUSCLE TENSED FOR ACTION. HE WAS NOT DISAPPOINTED! SUDDENLY, FLORY LEAPT, AND THE SCOUT WENT INTO ACTION WITH HIS FISTS!

SO YOU'VE COME OUT INTO THE OPEN AT LAST!

AA-GHH!

THE TOUGH, IRON-HARD SCOUT CAME TO IN A DAZE, AND MANAGED TO STRUGGLE UP ON DECK. BY THIS TIME THE BOAT HAD DRIFTED INTO THE BANK...

SMOKE AND HEAT SEARED KIT'S LUNGS. CHOKING AND GASPING, HE COLLAPSED TO THE DECK. AND AS THE SCOUT LAY THERE, THE FLAMES CLOSED ON THE POWDER KEGS...

BUT THUNDER, GALLOPING ALONG THE RIVER BANK, HAD SEEN HIS MASTER'S PLIGHT. AND AS THE BOAT DRIFTED INTO THE BANK HE LEAPT ON TO THE DECK...

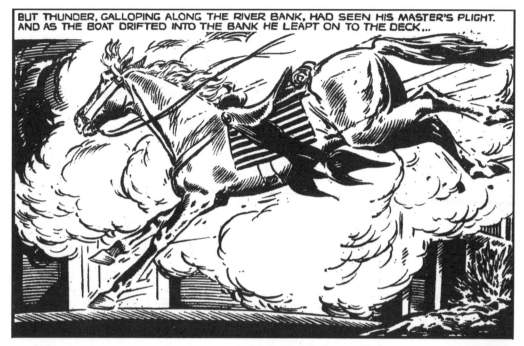

THE INTELLIGENT ANIMAL SENSED THE NEED FOR HASTE, AND DRAGGED KIT QUICKLY TO THE SIDE OF THE BOAT AND PUSHED HIM OVER THE GUNWALE. BUT ALREADY THE BOAT HAD DRIFTED AWAY FROM THE BANK INTO DEEPER WATER.

AS THE SCOUT FELL IN THE WATER, THUNDER PLUNGED AFTER HIM AND DRAGGED HIM TO SAFETY.

FOR A WHILE, KIT LAY MOTIONLESS ON THE BANK, BUT THEN THE FRESH AIR REVIVED HIM AND HE MANAGED TO STAGGER TO HIS FEET...

THEN, WITH A SHATTERING ROAR THE *SOUTHERN BELLE* BLEW UP... AND KIT WAS HURLED TO THE GROUND BY THE TERRIFIC BLAST...

STRAWN AND HIS PARDS WERE BY THIS TIME WELL BEYOND THE REACH OF THE EXPLOSION...

WELL, THAT AIN'T BLOWN THE DAM, BUT IT'S SURE FIXED CARSON /

AFTER LISTENING TO KIT'S STORY, COLONEL DEXTER DEALT SUMMARILY WITH THE THREE RASCALLY TRADERS...

I'M SENDING YOU TREACHEROUS RENEGADES TO NEW ORLEANS FOR TRIAL — AND IF THEY DON'T HANG YOU, YOU'LL BE LUCKY!

THE NEXT DAY, YOUNG DEXTER ARRIVED BACK AT THE FORT AND AFTER THE COLONEL HAD WELCOMED HIS SON, HE THANKED THE TWO BRAVES WHO HAD BROUGHT HIM...

DISMOUNT FROM YOUR PONIES, MY FRIENDS. YOU MUST REST HERE WITH US, AS OUR BROTHERS!

KIT KNEW THEN THAT THIS WAS THE BEGINNING OF A REAL PEACE WITH THE INDIANS!

KANSAS KID AND THE
'Frisco Racketeers

DAN DREW, BOSS OF THE DOUBLE-D
RANCH AND HIS TOP HAND, THE
KANSAS KID, WERE ON THEIR WAY
TO SANTA FE FOLLOWING A LETTER
RECEIVED BY DAN FROM HIS OLD
FRIEND MAT SIMPSON. MAT, A
POLITICIAN, WAS RUNNING FOR STATE
SENATOR OF SAN FRANCISCO, AND
HE HAD ASKED DAN TO MAKE
ENQUIRIES ON A VISIT TO SANTA FE
BY HIS OPPONENT, SETH HARPER.

Chapter 1 ASSASSIN

THE DOUBLE-D RIDER CAUGHT UP WITH THEM AND HANDED DAN A LETTER WHICH HAD ARRIVED AT THE RANCH AFTER THEIR DEPARTURE.

...MISS MOLLY SAW IT HAD COME FROM SAN FRANCISCO, AN' THOUGHT I'D BEST BRING IT ON TO YOU, BOSS.

GOOD THING YOU DID, CURLY! SAYS HERE THAT MAT'S SON, YOUNG MAT, IS ARRIVING AT SANTA FE ON TOMORROW'S TRAIN. SEEMS HE'S BEEN IN SOME KIND OF TROUBLE... COMIN' OUT HERE TO REST UP...

ARRIVING IN SANTA FE, DAN AND THE KID FOUND THE TOWN IN A FEVER OF EXCITEMENT OVER THE IMPENDING VISIT OF SETH HARPER.

UH! THEY WOULDN'T BE SO EAGER TO WELCOME SETH HARPER IF THEY KNEW HIM AS I DO... THE DURN CROOK!

ONCE THEIR HORSES WERE STABLED, AND THEY HAD WASHED AND EATEN, DAN AND THE KID CALLED IN AT THE TOWN MARSHAL'S OFFICE . . .

YOU SURE HARPER'S NOT COMING FOR ANY SPECIAL REASON, HARRY?

IF HE IS, I DON'T KNOW ABOUT IT, DAN. IT'S JUST A GOODWILL VISIT. HARPER'S OUT AFTER VOTES, I GUESS . . .

LATER, WHEN THEY RETURNED TO THEIR HOTEL . . .

YOU SATISFIED ABOUT HARPER, DAN?

I GUESS SO, KANSAS. LOOKS LIKE A STRAIGHTFORWARD VOTE-CATCHIN' TRIP, ALL RIGHT. ALL WE GOT TO DO NOW IS TO MEET YOUNG MAT OFF THAT TRAIN TOMORROW. GOOD NIGHT . . .

THE NEXT MORNING DAN AND KANSAS WENT DOWN TO THE STATION. SETH HARPER'S SUPPORTERS WERE WAITING TO GIVE HIM A BIG WELCOME... EXCITEMENT ROSE AS THE TRAIN STEAMED SLOWLY TO A HALT...

LOOK FOR A TALL YOUNG HOMBRE WITH HIS ARM IN A SLING, KANSAS...

SURE, DAN.

WELCOM SENATOR SETH HAR

AS THE MAYOR AND THE CROWD SWEPT FORWARD TO WELCOME SENATOR HARPER AND HIS PARTY, KANSAS SPOTTED THE YOUNG MAN THEY WERE LOOKING FOR...

THERE HE IS, DAN...

YEP! THAT'S YOUNG MAT, ALL RIGHT!

THE PASSENGERS STAYING ON THE TRAIN CROWDED TO THE WINDOWS TO SEE THE FUN — ALL EXCEPT ONE ... WHO HAD. CAREFULLY LOCKED HIMSELF IN THE GUARDS' VAN AT THE END OF THE REAR CARRIAGE !

THIS JOB SHOULD BE EASY ! GUARD'S BUSY DOWN THE OTHER END OF THE TRAIN RIGHT NOW !

AS THE TRAIN SHUDDERED INTO MOTION AGAIN, THE MAN IN THE GUARDS' VAN RAISED HIS RIFLE AND TOOK CAREFUL AIM AT SOMEBODY ON THE PLATFORM ...

THE GUNMAN SQUEEZED THE TRIGGER, SLOWLY, DELIBERATELY ... AND THE CRACK OF THE CARBINE WAS LOST IN THE EXCITED NOISE FROM THE CROWD ...

... SURE ARE PROUD TO HAVE YOU, BOY ! YOUR PA AN' ME — WHAT ... !

AAARGH ...

WHAT IN BLAZES ...

NUMB WITH SHOCK AND HORROR, OLD DAN BENT OVER THE STRICKEN MAN WHO, BEFORE LAPSING INTO UNCONSCIOUSNESS, GASPED A NAME...

AARGH... HAR...HARPER...

TAKE IT EASY, SON! SOMEONE GET DOC FLETCHER, PRONTO!

MAYBE THE SHOT *WAS* MEANT FOR HARPER, DAN! IT GOT MAT IN THE BACK — SO IT MUST HAVE COME FROM THE TRAIN!

DOC FLETCHER WHO WAS AMONGST THE CROWD AT THE STATION, WAS SOON KNEELING BESIDE MAT. WHEN HE LOOKED UP, HIS FACE WAS GRAVE...

WHAT'S THE NEXT STOP FOR THAT TRAIN?

IT'S BAD, DAN — VERY BAD. WE'LL HAVE TO GET HIM TO MY PLACE.

W-W-WAGON MOUND...

MEANWHILE, ABOARD THE TRAIN, THE GUNMAN WAS HAVING TO THINK QUICKLY...THE GUARD HAD RETURNED SOONER THAN HE EXPECTED AND WAS HAMMERING ON THE GUARDS' VAN DOOR, HELD FAST BY A WEDGE...

HASTILY PUTTING THE RIFLE BEHIND ONE OF THE PACKING CASES, CASH, THE GUNMAN, REMOVED THE WEDGE HE HAD PUT BENEATH THE DOOR. NEXT MOMENT, THE GUARD, RAISING HIS VOICE IN ANGER, BURST IN...

...ER... HOLD IT JUST A MINUTE! DOOR'S STUCK, SOMEHOW— HOLD IT...

GOT TO HIDE THIS RIFLE SOME PLACE —FAST!

SAY, WHAT GOES ON, MISTER? IT'S AGAINST COMPANY RULES FOR PASSENGERS TO ENTER THIS VAN, IN CASE YOU DON'T KNOW...

ER... SORRY, GUARD! I-I JUST CAME IN TO SEE IF MY LUGGAGE WAS OKAY...

AS CASH WENT BACK INTO THE COMPARTMENT, THE OLD GUARD'S BROWS FURROWED WITH SUSPICION. HE HAD SMELLED THE TANG OF EXPLODED POWDER, AND BEGAN LOOKING AROUND THE VAN, UNTIL...

JIMMINY—A CARBINE! AND THAT HOMBRE MUST HAVE PUT IT HERE! GUESS I'D BETTER PUT IT BACK WHERE I FOUND IT AND KEEP WATCH!

UNAWARE THAT HE WAS BEING WATCHED, THE GUNMAN AWAITED HIS CHANCE TO RETRIEVE THE RIFLE. THEN, WHEN HE THOUGHT THE GUARD WAS IN ANOTHER COMPARTMENT, INSPECTING TICKETS, HE MADE HIS MOVE.

NOW'S MY CHANCE!

HE'S GOING TO THE VAN! I'LL WAIT A MOMENT, THEN SURPRISE HIM!

CASH WAS INDEED SURPRISED. HE WAS JUST TAKING THE RIFLE FROM BEHIND THE PACKING CASE, WHEN THE GUARDS'VAN DOOR SUDDENLY BURST OPEN...

YOU'VE GOT SOME EXPLAINING TO DO, MISTER...

THAT'S WHAT YOU THINK...

THE NEXT MOMENT CASH SWUNG THE RIFLE BUTT TO THE GUARD'S HEAD, SENDING HIM CRASHING BACK INTO THE HALF-OPEN DOOR...

THAT'LL KEEP YOU QUIET, YOU INTERFERIN' OLD FOOL!

AAAAGH!

NOT SATISFIED WITH HAVING RENDERED THE GUARD UNCONSCIOUS, CASH OPENED THE LOADING DOOR OF THE GUARDS' VAN AND DRAGGED THE STILL FIGURE TO THE OPENING.

RECKON IT'S SAFER TO GET THIS GUY RIGHT OUT OF THE WAY!

AND AS THE TRAIN SPED ON THROUGH THE HILLS, CASH HEAVED THE GUARD INTO SPACE...

THAT'LL TEACH HIM TO KEEP HIS NOSE OUT OF CASH GURNEY'S BUSINESS! CAN'T BE FAR FROM WAGON MOUND NOW—THEN I'LL BE ABLE TO GET CLEAR!

BUT CASH GURNEY WOULD NOT HAVE FELT AT EASE HAD HE KNOWN SOMEONE WAS ON HIS TRAIL . . .

SAY, EZRA, LOOK AT THAT HOMBRE! HE SURE MUST BE IN A HURRY!

KANSAS CROSSED THE CANYON AND HIT THE ROCKY HILL BEYOND. ONCE OVER THE TOP, HE CAUGHT SIGHT OF THE TRAIN ON ITS LONG DETOUR, AND KNEW HE COULD EQUAL ITS TIME TO WAGON MOUND. BUT HE ALSO CAUGHT SIGHT OF SOMETHING ELSE!

THERE SHE IS . . . SAY! LOOKS LIKE A BODY DOWN THERE BESIDE THE TRACK!

WITH THE THOUGHT THAT HE COULD TEND TO THE MAN IF STILL ALIVE AND THEN RIDE ON TO WAGON MOUND AND CATCH THE TRAIN AT THE END OF ITS HALF-HOUR HALT, KANSAS PLUNGED HIS HORSE DOWN THE STEEP SLOPE TOWARDS THE RAILWAY TRACK...

MAY JUST BE INJURED... AND I CAN HELP HIM!

LEAPING FROM HIS HORSE, KANSAS PULLED THE GUARD CLEAR OF THE TRACK AND THEN KNELT BESIDE HIM. SLOWLY THE OLD MAN'S EYES OPENED AND HE GASPED HIS STORY.

MEAN LOOKING GUY, HE WAS... FOUND HIM IN MY VAN... HE'D BEEN USING A RIFLE...

RECKON HE'S THE GUY I'M AFTER, OLD TIMER! TAKE IT EASY NOW... I'LL SEND HELP OUT TO YOU!

THE OLD MAN DESCRIBED THE PASSENGER — AND THE DESCRIPTION TALLIED PERFECTLY WITH THE GUARD'S STORY!

MIGHTY QUEER HOMBRE... HE BOARDED THE WESTBOUND AND WENT BACK THE WAY HE JUST COME!

HE BOUGHT A TICKET BACK TO SANTA FE, EH?

SURE DID!

LOCATING THE WAGON MOUND DOCTOR, KANSAS GUIDED HIM IN HIS BUGGY TO A POINT NOT FAR FROM WHERE THE INJURED GUARD LAY...

YOU'LL FIND THE GUARD IN THE SHADE OF SOME ROCKS, ABOUT A MILE DOWN THE TRACK, DOC... HE SHOULD BE ALL RIGHT, I GUESS! I'VE GOT TO GET BACK TO SANTA FE NOW ...SO-LONG!

SO-LONG...

Chapter 2 END OF A GUNMAN

ARRIVING BACK IN SANTA FE, KANSAS WENT STRAIGHT TO DAN, WHO LISTENED CAREFULLY AS HIS TOP-HAND OUTLINED THE EVENTS OF HIS TRIP TO WAGON MOUND...

...SO ALL WE GOT TO DO NOW IS TO FIND A MAN WE NEVER EVEN SEEN AMONGST ALL THE FOLKS CROWDED JUST NOW INTO SANTA FE...

WE'LL GET HIM, DAN. FIRST WE'LL GO TO THE STATION AND MAKE SURE HE DID GET OFF THE TRAIN. IF HE DID, HE MUST BE STAYING AT•ONE OF THE HOTELS...WE'LL GET HIM ALL RIGHT!

ON THEIR WAY TO THE STATION, THEY CALLED AT DOC FLETCHER'S PLACE TO SEE HOW YOUNG MAT WAS GETTING ON, AND AS KANSAS LOOKED DOWN AT THE STILL UNCONSCIOUS FIGURE, HE HAD AN IDEA...

...A MIRACLE HE AIN'T DEAD. HE WON'T BE ABLE TO TALK FOR DAYS. HE'S HURT BAD, DAN — REAL BAD!

I KNOW HE'S IN GOOD-HANDS, DOC. DO THE BEST YOU CAN...

DOC—IF ANYBODY ASKS, TELL THEM MAT'S DEAD! I WANT WHOEVER SHOT THE BOY TO THINK HE DID A REAL JOB!

THEN, AS THE GUNMAN TRIED TO GET IN A SECOND SHOT, THE KID'S FIST FLAILED TO HIS JAW...

AARGGHH...

A TICKET FROM WAGON MOUND TO SANTA FE! AN' BEARING TODAY'S DATE! RECKON HE'S THE GUY WE WANT, KANSAS!

CASH'S EYES BULGED WITH TERROR AS KANSAS DRAGGED HIM TO HIS FEET...

THAT OLD MAN YOU PUSHED OFF THE TRAIN CAN IDENTIFY YOU, IF NEEDS BE...NOW START TALKING! WHY DID YOU SHOOT AT YOUNG MAT SIMPSON?

HOLD IT...I'LL TELL YOU WHAT I KNOW...

BUT SOMEONE ELSE WAS INTERESTED IN THE GUNMAN ...THE MAN WHO HAD BEEN SHADOWING KANSAS AND DAN! IN THE ALLEYWAY ALONGSIDE THE SALOON, HE PEERED THROUGH A WINDOW ...AND HIS HAND REACHED FOR A GUN HIDDEN INSIDE HIS JACKET...

GOOD THING I TRAILED THOSE TWO...GURNEY SEEMS REAL SCARED ...SCARED ENOUGH TO TALK!

GURNEY HAD REGAINED HIS BREATH AND WAS ABOUT TO TELL HIS STORY, WHEN... A BULLET SUDDENLY CLOSED HIS LIPS!

I WAS HIRED FOR THE SHOOTING IN SAN FRANCISCO— HONEST! I NEVER SAW YOUNG SIMPSON BEFORE IN MY... AAARGHHHH!

DAN— LOOK OUT!

THE WINDOW...

KANSAS BURST THROUGH THE BATSWING DOORS OF THE SALOON, BUT THE MAN WHO HAD SILENCED CASH GURNEY WAS LOST IN THE NIGHT...

THE FELLER INSIDE WON'T TALK AGAIN! THE BARKEEPER HAS SENT FOR THE SHERIFF... RECKON WE'D BEST KEEP QUIET ABOUT THIS BUSINESS!

HE GOT CLEAR AWAY, DARN IT!

Chapter 3 DANGEROUS JOURNEY

AS THE SWAYING TRAIN CHUGGED ALONG THE ENDLESS MILES OF SINGLE TRACK, DEL SLATER BEGAN TO WONDER WHY KANSAS WAS ON THE TRAIN.

PERHAPS GURNEY DID SAY SOMETHING... MEBBE THIS GUY KNOWS MORE THAN WE THINK...

GRADUALLY, SLATER CONVINCED HIMSELF THAT THE SAFEST COURSE WAS TO GET RID OF THE KANSAS KID... AND LATER IN THE DAY HE WAS GIVEN THE OPPORTUNITY...

...COMING UP TO THE WOODPILE, GENTLEMEN... WILL ABLE-BODIED MEN GIVE A HAND TO LOAD UP, PLEASE...

I GUESS THAT MEANS YOU AND ME, STRANGER...

HUGE WOODPILES WERE STACKED AT INTERVALS ALONG THE RAIL TRACK BY CONTRACTORS, AND MALE PASSENGERS WERE EXPECTED TO GIVE A HAND LOADING THEM ON TO THE TRAIN...

COFFEE ON THE COMPANY WHEN YOU'RE DONE, GENTLEMEN.

AS THE MEN SET TO WORK, SLATER WORKED HIS WAY DOWN TO THE END OF THE STOCKPILE, AND A WORKMAN'S AXE HE SAW THERE GAVE HIM A SUDDEN IDEA!

AN AXE! JUST THE THING! CAN'T RISK A GUNSHOT... AND I'VE GOT TO GET RID OF THAT BUSYBODY, KANSAS!

SNARLING WITH RAGE, SLATER CLAWED AT HIS SHOULDER HOLSTER, BUT THE KID WAS UP ON HIS FEET IN A FLASH... AND HIS FIST SWUNG TO THE OUTLAW'S JAW...

SNARLING WITH RAGE, SLATER STAGGERED TO HIS FEET AND FLUNG HIMSELF AT KANSAS... BUT THE COWBOY'S FIST DROVE INTO HIS JAW FOR A SECOND TIME AND HE REELED BACKWARDS, HALF UNCONSCIOUS...

SO... ANOTHER KILLER... WELL, YOU'RE GOING TO TALK, MISTER— AND TALK PLENTY!

AAAGH... WAIT... NO...

SLATER HAD HAD ENOUGH PUNISHMENT AND AS KANSAS DRAGGED HIM UP, HE BABBLED HOARSELY...

ALL RIGHT, MISTER— WHY DID YOU HAVE YOUNG SIMPSON KILLED?

I DIDN'T HAVE HIM KILLED... HONEST! IT WAS THE BOSS'S ORDERS ...I HAD NOTHIN' TO DO WITH IT!

WITH THE ROAR OF AN APPROACHING TRAIN GROWING LOUDER IN THEIR EARS, KANSAS SHOOK THE MAN, HOPING TO MAKE HIM TELL ALL HE KNEW...

WHO IS THIS BOSS OF YOURS? C'MON, SPEAK...

I CAN'T TELL YOU — I CAN'T! HE'D HAVE ME KILLED! HE'D...

SUDDENLY, WITH A FIERCE STRENGTH BORN OF SHEER DESPERATION SLATER LUNGED FORWARD, STRIVING TO PUSH KANSAS UNDER THE WHEELS OF AN APPROACHING TRAIN!

LATER, WHEN THE TRAIN WAS WELL ON ITS WAY AGAIN, KANSAS SPOKE WITH THE MAN WHO SAID HE HAD SEEN SLATER IN SAN FRANCISCO...

HE WAS A DEALER IN FARINO'S GAMBLING JOINT...

FARINO'S, EH? THANKS, MISTER, I'LL REMEMBER THAT!

WHEN LATER, THE NEXT DAY, THE TRAIN DREW INTO SAN FRANCISCO, KANSAS THANKED SUE TRAVERS ONCE AGAIN FOR HER TIMELY WARNING.

...I WOULD HAVE BEEN KILLED IF IT HADN'T BEEN FOR YOU...

OH, IT WAS NOTHING ...GOODBYE! PERHAPS WE'LL MEET AGAIN SOMETIME!

Chapter 4 CROOKED DEALER

DAN HAD ARRANGED BY TELEGRAPH FOR HIS OLD FRIEND, MAT SIMPSON, TO MEET KANSAS OUTSIDE THE RAILWAY DEPOT IN A QUIET SIDE STREET...

KANSAS, WELCOME TO SAN FRANCISCO! THAT'S MY BROUGHAM ACROSS THE WAY...

HOWDY, MISTER SIMPSON...

SIMPSON TOOK KANSAS OUT TO HIS BIG HOUSE ON WEALTHY NOB HILL. THERE, AFTER A GOOD MEAL, THEY TALKED...

...SO THERE'S NO REASON WHY ANYONE SHOULD WANT TO KILL YOUNG MAT...

HE WAS KIND OF WILD, PERHAPS — GAMBLED A BIT, BUT ALWAYS PAID HIS DEBTS... AT LEAST, I DID! BUT SOMEONE HERE TOOK A SHOT AT HIM A FEW WEEKS AGO...

KANSAS THEN HEARD HOW YOUNG MAT, BECAUSE OF HIS WILD LIVING, HAD BECOME AN EMBARRASSMENT TO HIS FATHER'S CAMPAIGN TO BE ELECTED STATE SENATOR...

AFTER THE SHOOTING, I FIGURED IT MIGHT BE BEST TO SEND HIM OUT WEST TO OLD DAN'S PLACE FOR A SPELL...

...AND THE KILLERS FOLLOWED HIM ALL THE WAY OUT THERE! THEY MUST WANT TO GET HIM AWFUL BAD!

LATER KANSAS GOT UP TO GO, REFUSING MAT'S OFFER OF A ROOM AT THE HOUSE...

NO, THANKS, SIR. I GUESS I'D BETTER STAY AT A HOTEL. NO USE EVERYBODY KNOWING I'M WORKING ON THIS THING!

YOU'RE RIGHT, BOY. BUT WAIT— LET ME GET YOU SOME OF MAT'S CLOTHES. YOU STAND OUT A MILE IN THAT RIG!

BACK IN HIS HOTEL ROOM, KANSAS TRIED ON THE CLOTHES MAT HAD GIVEN HIM AND DECIDED TO START RIGHT AWAY WITH A VISIT TO FARINO'S!

BY HOKEY— NEVER THOUGHT I COULD LOOK SO SMART! NO TIME LIKE NOW FOR A CALL ON THIS HERE FARINO PLACE, I GUESS!

KANSAS QUICKLY DISCOVERED HIS WAY TO FARINO'S!

FARINO'S? SURE! THAT'S IT, RIGHT ACROSS THE WAY THERE. I HOPE YOU GOT PLENTY MONEY TO SPARE, FRIEND!

THANKS, MISTER—I GUESS I CAN AFFORD TO LOOK INSIDE, ANYWAY!

KANSAS KNEW THAT THE DEALER HAD PALMED A QUEEN OF SPADES —AND THAT THERE MUST BE ANOTHER IN THE PACK . . .

WE GOT A TROUBLE SHOOTER, HARRY . . .

ALL RIGHT, MISTER — WHAT GOES ON ?

THE DEALER HERE'S GOING TO DEAL OUT THE PACK, FACE UP, SO WE CAN SEE HOW HE USES TWO QUEENS OF SPADES —THAT'S WHAT GOES ON, FRIEND.

THE STRONG-ARM MAN THEN MADE WHAT WAS PROBABLY THE BIGGEST MISTAKE OF HIS LIFE . . . HE LAID HANDS ON THE KANSAS KID ! KANSAS' FIST SHOT OUT, TAKING THE MAN FULL IN THE MIDRIFF . . .

C'MON, MISTER, YOU'RE LEAVING . . . AARGH . . .

NOT YET, FRIEND —

THIS WAS EXACTLY WHAT KANSAS HAD WANTED! AS LEW FARINO LED HIM TOWARDS THE REAR OF THE PREMISES, KANSAS RECOGNISED THE GIRL SINGING ON THE STAGE. IT WAS THE GIRL HE HAD MET ON THE TRAIN.

THE SINGER... IT'S MISS SUE TRAVERS!

IN FARINO'S OFFICE ...

THERE'S YOUR MONEY, MISTER. TAKE IT, AND LEAVE.

I'M NOT THROUGH PLAYING YET, FARINO...

YOU HEARD WHAT THE BOSS SAID... BEAT IT! AND DON'T NEVER COME BACK!

ALTHOUGH KANSAS STILL HAD NO REAL PROOF, HE NOW KNEW THAT LEW FARINO HAD SOMETHING TO DO WITH THE TWO GUNMEN, CASH AND SLATER . . .

I'M A FRIEND OF YOUNG MAT SIMPSON'S, FARINO — THAT'S WHO I AM. AND I AIM TO FIND OUT WHY HE WAS SHOT AND WHO DID IT. THAT ANSWER YOUR QUESTION?

I'VE NEVER EVEN HEARD OF SIMPSON, AND YOU CAN'T PROVE THAT I HAVE!

KANSAS KNEW THAT FARINO WAS RIGHT — AT THE MOMENT. BUT HE GRINNED EASILY. HIS GUN TRAINED ON THE TWO MEN AS HE MOVED BACK TO OPEN A DOOR WHICH HE GUESSED WAS A QUICK WAY OUT OF THE BUILDING.

OFFICE

NOT RIGHT NOW, FARINO — BUT I WILL! MEANWHILE, STAY WHERE YOU ARE TILL I GET CLEAR — OR I'LL SHOOT!

SUE KNEW AT ONCE THAT FARINO WAS TALKING ABOUT KANSAS. THEN, SUDDENLY, THE DOOR OF THE OFFICE WAS THROWN OPEN AND MAX, THE STRONG ARM MAN, FOLLOWED BY THE OWNER OF THE GAMBLING HOUSE, HURRIED OUT. FARINO STOPPED SHORT AS HE SAW SUE THERE, AND MAX DISAPPEARED THROUGH A SIDE DOOR INTO THE NIGHT.

ER...ER... MISTER FARINO — ABOUT THAT PIANO PLAYER...

NOT NOW, GIRL, I'M BUSY! SEE YOU LATER!

SENSING THAT SOMETHING VERY STRANGE WAS HAPPENING, SUE DID NOT STRAY VERY FAR FROM FARINO'S SIGHT. AND WHEN MAX RETURNED, SHE MADE CERTAIN SHE WAS WITHIN EARSHOT!

I FOUND HIM, BOSS! HE'S STAYIN' AT THE ADELPHI!

GOOD, MAX, GOOD! WAIT FOR ME IN THE OFFICE...

THE NEXT MOMENT KANSAS HAD SWUNG THE MAN ROUND AND DELIVERED A PILE-DRIVING BLOW TO HIS JAW. MAX REELED BACK, THE KNIFE FLYING FROM HIS HAND...

GROANING, THE BATTERED MAX STRUGGLED BACK TO CONSCIOUSNESS AS KANSAS EMPTIED A JUG OF WATER OVER HIS HEAD...

WAKE UP, RAT! WE'RE GOING VISITING!

AAA...

KANSAS NOW KNEW THAT FARINO WAS BEHIND THE GUNMEN, AND NO SOONER HAD HE LEFT THE GAMBLER'S OFFICE THAN FARINO WAS HOLSTERING A GUN AND LEAVING HIMSELF...

THIS IS SOMETHING THE BIG BOSS WILL HAVE TO INTERRUPT HIS SLEEP FOR!

OUTSIDE, KANSAS WAS WAITING IN THE SHADOWS...AND WATCHING. HE SAW LEW FARINO HURRY OUT INTO THE WIDE, DESERTED STREET...

IT WORKED! FARINO ISN'T THE BOSS, AND HE'S GOING TO SEE WHOEVER IT IS RIGHT NOW!

Chapter 5 BROUGHT TO JUSTICE

KANSAS TRAILED FARINO THROUGH THE DESERTED CITY AND SAW HIM ENTER A BIG MANSION ON THE OTHER SIDE OF TOWN...

SO THIS IS WHERE THE BIG BOSS LIVES! IT WOULDN'T BE SAFE FOR ME TO GO ANY FURTHER NOW. I'LL SEE OLD MAT SIMPSON TOMORROW AND FIND OUT WHO LIVES IN THIS MAGNIFICENT HACIENDA!

PLEASED WITH HIS NIGHT'S WORK, KANSAS RETURNED TO HIS HOTEL. NEXT MORNING, WITH OLD MAT SIMPSON, HE RODE PAST THE HOUSE TO WHICH FARINO HAD HURRIED THE NIGHT BEFORE.

THAT'S SENATOR HARPER'S HOUSE, WE SUSPECTED HARPER WAS BEHIND THE BIG CRIME IN THE CITY, BUT THERE'S NEVER BEEN A SCRAP OF PROOF. HE'S BEEN TOO CLEVER!

BUT HE MUST HAVE THOUGHT YOUNG MATT KNEW SOMETHING ...THAT'S WHY HE WANTED HIM KILLED!

KANSAS RE-LOCKED THE DOOR, THEN SUE KNOCKED AT FARINO'S OFFICE, CALLING OUT HER NAME. WHEN THE DOOR OPENED AND MAX, THE GUNMAN, APPEARED, KANSAS MOVED!

WHAT IS IT, LADY? WE'RE BUSY— AAAGGHHH...

WHITE, SPEECHLESS AND MOANING WITH FURY, FARINO LOOKED ONCE AGAIN AT THE GUN OF THE MAN HE HAD COME TO HATE!

YOU!

HOLD IT RIGHT THERE, FARINO! WHAT'S THE MATTER, FRIEND? YOU DON'T SEEM GLAD TO SEE ME!

AS FARINO TALKED OF HIS ASSOCIATION WITH SENATOR HARPER AND THE GUNMAN WHO HAD TRIED TO KILL YOUNG MAT SIMPSON SENATOR HARPER BURST INTO THE ROOM... BROUGHT THERE BY KANSAS' LETTER, ACCUSING HIM OF BEING BEHIND THE CITY'S CRIME...

WHAT'S THIS, FARINO? YOU BUNGLING FOOL! FIRST YOU MESS UP THE SIMPSON SHOOTING, NOW THIS KANSAS FELLER—SAY, WHAT GOES—

GREAT JUMPING JIMMINY...

TOO LATE THE CROOKED POLITICIAN WHIRLED AND SAW THE TRAP SET FOR HIM. SNARLING, HE CLAWED FOR A GUN... BUT KANSAS QUICKLY OVERPOWERED HIM...

TOO LATE, SENATOR— YOU'VE COME TO THE END OF THE LINE!

JEEHOSEPHAT! THIS IS THE STORY OF THE CENTURY!

ALL RIGHT, FARINO— LET'S TAKE YOU DOWN TO THE CITY JAIL!

COWBOY PICTURE LIBRARY
WESTERN SCRAPBOOK

THE HUGE WAGONS WHICH CROSSED THE WESTERN FRONTIER TO THE NEW AND FERTILE LANDS OF CALIFORNIA AND OREGON WERE BUILT VERY HIGH OFF THE GROUND SO THAT THEY WOULD NOT CATCH IN TREE STUMPS AND JUTTING ROCKS. THE INSIDES OF THE PRAIRIE SCHOONERS WERE USUALLY ROUNDED SO THAT STORES AND CARGO WOULD NOT SLIP WHILST GOING UP HILL. ALSO THE WAGON FLOORS WERE WATER TIGHT SO THAT THEY COULD FLOAT ACROSS THE RIVERS AND STREAMS CROSSING THE TRAILS.

WHEN SIX THIEVES STOLE HIS STOCK OF HORSES, JOHN R. HUGHES, LATER TO BECOME FAMOUS AS CAPTAIN OF THE TEXAS RANGERS, TRAILED THE BANDITS FOR OVER A YEAR. FINALLY HE CAUGHT UP WITH THEM AND SENT THEM TO JAIL. HE ALSO RETURNED WITH MOST OF HIS STOLEN HORSES.

ALTHOUGH HE OWNED A HUGE, COMFORTABLE BED WITH A SPRING MATTRESS, JOHN CHISUM, "THE CATTLE KING OF NEW MEXICO" ALWAY SLEPT ON A BLANKET ON THE FLOOR, OR OUTSIDE HIS PALATIAL RANCH HOUSE. THE BED WAS JUST FOR SHOW.

TO MOST INDIANS, RED WAS A SACRED COLOUR. BUT DESPITE THIS, THE INDIANS NEVER FOUND A WAY TO MAKE IT FROM THE NATURAL RESOURCES OFFERED TO THEM AND THEY WOULD ATTACK A SETTLER'S HOMESTEAD, JUST TO GET VERMILION PAINT TO DECORATE THEIR FACES.

TO PROTECT THE WAGONS, A WEST BOUND TRAIN WOULD OFTEN TAKE ALONG ONE OR TWO HEAVY CANNONS MOUNTED ON WHEELS. THESE PROVED VERY EFFECTIVE AGAINST THE WARRING REDSKINS.

THE FIRST MAN TO TAKE A WAGON TRAIN SUCCESSFULLY THROUGH THE MAJESTIC ROCKY MOUNTAIN PEAKS WAS CAPTAIN BONNEVILLE.

A GREAT DANGER TO HORSES WERE THE GOPHER HOLES' DOTTED OVER THE PLAINS AND PRAIRIES. THESE HOLES WERE MADE BY A LITTLE MOLE-LIKE ANIMAL CALLED A GOPHER, AND ALTHOUGH THESE TINY CREATURES WERE A BOON TO FARMERS, FOR THEY MADE NATURAL IRRIGATION CHANNELS, THEY WERE A MENACE TO THE PLAINSMAN AND COWBOY.

WHEN THE HUGE CATTLE DRIVES TO THE NORTH BEGAN, A MAN NAMED DICK WOOTEN HAD AN INGENIOUS IDEA. HE SET UP A TOLL-GATE ON THE ONLY TRAIL THROUGH THE MOUNTAINS OF COLORADO AND COLLECTED TEN CENTS FOR EVERY HERD OF CATTLE WHICH PASSED THROUGH THE TOLL. BUT SOON THE CATTLE OWNERS FOUND AN ALTERNATIVE ROUTE, NOT HOWEVER BEFORE WOOTEN HAD MADE A CONSIDERABLE FORTUNE.

TOLL
10¢

BUCK JONES and the Apache Manhunt

THE WHITE MEN CALLED THEM APACHE ~~ ENEMY. OF ALL THE CRUEL RED PEOPLE OF THE DESERT, THEY WERE THE CRUELLEST. IT TOOK GRIM YEARS OF BLOODSHED IN THE GREAT SOUTH-WEST TO CURB THE APACHE APPETITE FOR SCALPS.

THE TONTO BASIN IN ARIZONA HAD BEEN CLEARED OF APACHES BACK IN THE SEVENTIES BY THE FAMOUS GENERAL GEORGE CROOK. NOW THE TONTO APACHES LIVED ON THEIR TRIBAL RESERVATION IN THE WHITE MOUNTAINS, RULED BY A WISE AND PEACE-LOVING CHIEF, NANTAHE. BUT NANTAHE WAS OLD ~~ THE SULLEN APACHE PRIDE STILL BURNED DEEP ~~ AND THERE WERE MEN HUNGRY TO AWAKEN IT...

Chapter 1 BLACK KNIFE

ONE OF THESE BITTER MEN WAS CALLED CUCHILLO NEGRO, OR BLACK KNIFE, BY THE APACHES. HATRED WAS CARVED DEEP INTO HIS FACE. NOW, WHILE OLD NANTAHE WEARILY LISTENED IN THE LIVID SUNLIGHT, BLACK KNIFE TAUNTED THE TONTO BRAVES WITH BARBED WORDS.

THE WHITE MAN HAS STOLEN YOUR LANDS! HE HAS ALSO STOLEN THE WARM BLOOD FROM YOUR VEINS THAT YOU SIT UNDER THE TENT-POLES WITH THE SQUAWS WHILE THERE ARE MANY SCALPS TO BE TAKEN!

FOR MANY MOONS, BLACK KNIFE HAD TEMPTED THE YOUNG BUCKS OF THE TONTO APACHES WITH THE SAME HARSH WORDS...

TAKE YOUR RIFLES, O TONTO BRAVES! LEAVE THIS RESERVATION WHICH IS YOUR CAGE! FOLLOW ME, AND KILL THE PINDA LICK-O-YI, THE WHITE EYES!

CHIEF NANTAHE HAD FOUGHT AGAINST THE WHITE MEN LONG AGO AT THE SIDE OF SUCH FAMOUS TONTO WARRIORS AS DEL-SHE, AND CHUNTZ, AND NAQUINAQUIS. NOW HE LIFTED HIS PROUD HEAD AND SPOKE TO HIS PEOPLE...

MY PEOPLE, DO NOT LISTEN TO BLACK KNIFE! HIS HEAD IS HOT AND HIS EYE IS BLIND WITH ANGER! THE TIME OF KILLING IS PAST!

FOR NANTAHE IT IS PAST, O BRAVES! HE IS OLD, AND HIS BLOOD IS THIN! BUT YOU ARE YOUNG AND THE WAR DRUM SPEAKS TO YOU!

BLACK KNIFE'S VOICE WAS SHRILL, BUT THE TONTO BRAVES SHOOK THEIR HEADS. NANTAHE WAS THEIR CHIEF. HE HAD TOLD THEM TO STAY ON THEIR RESERVATION, AND THEY WOULD STAY.

YES, MY PEOPLE, I AM OLD! WHEN I WAS YOUNG MY HEART BURNED AGAINST THE WHITE MAN! NOW I HAVE LEARNED THAT HE IS THE FRIEND OF OUR PEOPLE!

NANTAHE'S WORDS ARE THE WORDS OF WISDOM!

THE WHITE MAN WILL NOT HARM US IF WE OBEY HIS LAWS. CLOSE YOUR EARS TO THE VOICE OF BLACK KNIFE!

THROUGH THE NARROW ENTRANCE INTO THE TONTO VILLAGE GALLOPED THE RUSTLERS, GUNS BLAZING. THE OLD APACHE ON GUARD THERE WOKE WITH A START AS THE PONIES BEGAN TO REAR AND PLUNGE...

HI-YAAA!

OUT OF OUR WAY, SCUM!

THE TONTO BRAVES HAD SPRUNG UP IN ALARM AT THE SOUND OF THE GUNS. BLACK KNIFE WAS SCREAMING AT THEM NOW, HIS EYES GLITTERING WITH RAGE...

SEE! THESE ARE THE WHITE MEN YOU TRUSTED, FOOLS!

AYEE! THEY DRIVE OUR PONIES BEFORE THEM!

THE TONTO BRAVES WERE UNARMED, BUT THE PONIES WERE THEIR MOST PRIZED POSSESSIONS. DESPERATELY THEY FLUNG THEMSELVES AT THE WHITE RUSTLERS...

KEEP GOING, MEN! RIDE THE CURS DOWN!

NOW THE PONIES WERE SWEEPING TOWARDS THE BUFFALO-HIDE LODGES AND THE CREEK, HERDED BY THE GUNS OF THE RUSTLERS. GRIM-FACED BUT HELPLESS, THE TWO WHITE MEN WATCHED...

IT'S THE SPUR GANG!

WHOEVER THEY ARE, THEY'RE PLAYING INTO BLACK KNIFE'S HANDS. THE TONTOS WON'T LIKE THIS ONE LITTLE BIT!

STARING-EYED, THE TONTO BRAVES CHOKED IN THE DUST OF THE RUSTLERS ~~ AND LISTENED WITH GROWING ANGER TO THE HARSH WORDS OF BLACK KNIFE...

PINCATO' IS DEAD, BROTHERS!

DID I NOT WARN YOU, O BRAVES! THIS IS THE WHITE MAN'S LAW ~~ TO STEAL THE TONTO'S PONIES, TO BEAT THE TONTOS ~~ TO KILL THE TONTOS...

BLACK KNIFE'S WORDS ARE JUST, BROTHERS!

THROUGH THE PEACEFUL TONTO VILLAGE, TOPPLING THE TALL BUFFALO-HIDE LODGES, SMASHED THE GRINNING RUSTLERS WITH THEIR WILD-MANED BOOTY.

HEAD THE PONIES WEST, MEN. KEEP THEM MOVING!

THIS IS EASIER THAN SNEAKING CATTLE AWAY AROUND ALKALI, EH, CAD?

Chapter 2 ENTER VIRGIL SALT

ALKALI CITY LAY ON THE PLAINS OF ARIZONA THIRTY MILES FROM THE WHITE MOUNTAIN RESERVATION OF THE TONTO APACHES. THE SUN WAS WESTERING WHEN A FAT MAN ON A LATHERED HORSE RODE FURIOUSLY INTO MAIN STREET.

IT'S MOSS CLUTTON! WHAT'S HE ALL STEAMED UP ABOUT?

SHERIFF! SHERIFF!

BUCK JONES, ALKALI CITY'S PEACE OFFICER, GOT GRIMLY TO HIS FEET...

THE SPUR BOYS, SHERIFF ~~ I JUST SEEN THEM RAIDING THE TONTO RESERVATION UP IN WHITE MOUNTAIN!

SO!

BREATHLESSLY, THE FAT MOSS CLUTTON TOLD HIS GRIM STORY...

THEY RUSTLED THE PONIES RIGHT OUT OF THAT VILLAGE IN BROAD DAYLIGHT, SHERIFF. THE TONTOS ARE HOPPING MAD. A HOTHEAD CALLED BLACK KNIFE HAS PUT A BULLET IN JIM SCOTT AND THE WHOLE DANGED TRIBE IS HITTING THE WARPATH!

APACHES ARE THE ARMY'S RESPONSIBILITY! I'LL TELEGRAPH CAPTAIN VEILE AT FORT WHIPPLE ~~ BUT I'LL LOOK AFTER CAD SPUR AND HIS MEN MYSELF...

THE SPUR GANG HAD BEEN OPERATING ON THE RANGES AROUND ALKALI CITY FOR MANY MONTHS. THOUGH BUCK JONES HAD BRUSHED WITH THEM SEVERAL TIMES, HE HAD FAILED TO FIND THEIR HIDE-OUT. BUT NOW THE COLD GREY EYES OF ALKALI'S FIGHTING SHERIFF BODED ILL FOR THE RUSTLERS...

YOU AIN'T GOING AFTER THE SPUR BOYS WITHOUT A POSSE, ARE YOU, SHERIFF?

NOPE. I'M JUST GOING TO HAVE A LOOK-SEE!

THE SUNSET WAS GILDING THE TIN ROOFS OF THE COW-TOWN WHEN BUCK JONES HEADED HIS HORSE FOR THE DISTANT MOUNTAIN RANGES...

IF I CAN PICK UP THE TRAIL LEFT BY THOSE TONTO PONIES, IT SHOULD LEAD ME RIGHT TO CAD SPUR'S HIDEOUT...

TWO HOURS LATER, AS HE WAS RIDING WARILY THROUGH THE FOOTHILLS OF WHITE MOUNTAIN, BUCK JONES REINED IN SHARPLY. IT WAS DARK NOW, AND A CAMP FIRE GLEAMED AMONG THE ROCKS AHEAD...

HALLO...

DISMOUNTING, BUCK SLID FORWARD AS SOFTLY AS A SHADOW. THERE WAS ONLY ONE MAN WRAPPED IN A RUG BESIDE THE DYING FIRE. HE SEEMED TO BE ASLEEP...

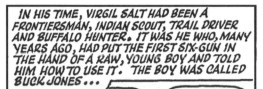

IN HIS TIME, VIRGIL SALT HAD BEEN A FRONTIERSMAN, INDIAN SCOUT, TRAIL DRIVER AND BUFFALO HUNTER. IT WAS HE WHO, MANY YEARS AGO, HAD PUT THE FIRST SIX-GUN IN THE HAND OF A RAW, YOUNG BOY AND TOLD HIM HOW TO USE IT. THE BOY WAS CALLED BUCK JONES...

YOU LIE IN YOUR BEARD, OLD-TIMER! I DIDN'T MAKE A SOUND THAT A MAN WITH HUMAN EARS WOULD HEAR~~ YOU TAUGHT ME BETTER THAN THAT! BUT I THOUGHT YOU WERE HUNTING BUFFALO IN KANSAS?

SO I WAS ~~ TILL THE BUFFALO QUIT! AIN'T SEEN HAIR NOR HIDE OF ONE IN NINE MONTHS ~~ ONLY THEIR BONES!

THE SMILE DIED FROM THE TOUGH OLD FACE OF THE FRONTIERSMAN.

SOME OF THE HUNTERS ARE STAYING UP IN KANSAS AS BONE-PICKERS ~~ NOT ME! I SWOPPED MY SHARPS FIFTY FOR A WINCHESTER AND RODE WEST AFTER THE BUFFALO AND ~~ WAAL, I'M STILL RIDING!

BUCK JONES FROWNED...

BUFFALO HAVE GONE FROM ARIZONA, TOO, VIRGIL. MAYBE THERE'S A HERD LEFT IN COMANCHE COUNTRY ~~ I WOULDN'T KNOW...

SURE, THE BUFFALO HAVE GONE! ONCE THEY WAS AS THICK ON THE PLAINS AS GRASS ~~ BUT THAT WAS WHEN I WAS YOUNG AND YOU WAS THE KID I TAUGHT TO HANDLE A HORSE AND A GUN! NOW I'M GETTING OLD, AND IT SEEMS TO ME SOMETIMES I OUGHT TO BE GOING WHERE THE BUFFALO'S GONE...

WHEN BUCK JONES HEADED HIS HORSE NORTH AGAIN, OLD VIRGIL SALT RODE AT HIS SIDE.

THE SPUR BOYS RUSTLED A PACK OF TONTO PONIES FROM THE RESERVATION TODAY. IF WE CAN PICK UP THEIR TRAIL IT MAY LEAD TO THE GANG'S HIDEOUT!

PONY TRAIL, DID YOU SAY? LOOKIT HERE...

IT WAS VIRGIL SALT WHO FIRST SAW THE TELL-TALE MARKS OF MANY HOOVES IN THE SOFT SAND OF THE TRAIL AHEAD. NOW HE SLID FROM HIS SADDLE TO READ THE SECRET OF THOSE MARKS WITH A LIFETIME OF SCOUT-LORE IN HIS SHREWD OLD EYES...

SEE WHICH WAY THEM BENT GRASS STALKS IS POINTING, YOUNG JONES? AND THE MITE OF DUST THAT'S BLOWN INTO THESE UNSHOD HOOF-MARKS. INJUN PONIES ~~ HEADING WEST ~~ TWO-THREE HOURS SINCE!

BUCK JONES GRINNED. HE COULD READ THOSE SIGNS HIMSELF, BUT HE WASTED NO TIME PROVING IT. SWIFTLY AND SILENTLY HE RODE ON ALONG THE RUSTLERS' TRAIL...

THAT'S CRAZY HORSE CANYON AHEAD ~~ AND THE TRACKS LEAD STRAIGHT INTO IT! I DON'T AIM TO TAKE ON THE SPUR BOYS TONIGHT, BUT I'D SURE LIKE TO MAKE CERTAIN THEY'RE HOLED UP HERE...

DAVE NAGLE HAD COUNTED ON KNOCKING OUT THE LAWMAN IN THAT FIRST BRUTAL DIVE, BUT BUCK JONES TOOK THE LUNGING FIST ON HIS SHOULDER...

COME OUT, DRAT YOU!

THEN BUCK JONES GOT BOTH FEET AGAINST THE RUSTLER'S CHEST~~ FLEXED HIS POWERFUL LEG MUSCLES~~ AND KICKED...

AAGH!

NOW THE SHERIFF'S OWN COLT ROARED~~ WITH DEADLY EFFECT...

ONE OF THE RUSTLERS HAD FALLEN INTO THE SURE HANDS OF BUCK JONES. THE OTHERS WOULD PROBABLY BE CELEBRATING THEIR SUCCESSFUL RAID IN THEIR CANYON HIDEOUT, UNAWARE THAT THE FIGHTING LAWMAN HAD SMOKED THEM OUT...

OKAY, NAGLE! I'M TAKING YOU TO ALKALI! I'LL COME BACK FOR YOUR FRIENDS WITH A POSSE LATER!

SMART SHOOTING, YOUNG JONES! DANGED IF I KNOW WHAT MADE ME MISS!

WITH THE SUBDUED DAVE NAGLE MOUNTED IN FRONT OF HIM, BUCK JONES MADE TRACKS FOR ALKALI. FOR MOST OF THE WAY, OLD VIRGIL SALT WAS SILENT. THEN...

BUCK JONES GLANCED SYMPATHETICALLY AT HIS FRIEND. OLD AGE MIGHT BE ROBBING VIRGIL SALT OF THE RAZOR-KEEN SENSES WHICH HAD MADE HIM A DEADLY INDIAN SCOUT IN HIS YOUTH ON THE WILD FRONTIER, BUT HE WOULD NEVER ADMIT IT...

RECKON MY HOSS MUST HAVE JINKED JUST AS I SQUEEZED THE TRIGGER...

STILL WORRYING ABOUT THAT SHOT YOU MISSED, OLD-TIMER?

WHO SAYS I'M WORRYING. I STILL GOT THE SHARPEST PAIR OF EYES IN THIS TERRITORY!

SURE YOU HAVE, VIRGIL!

THE DAWN SUN WAS SCRUBBING THE DUSTY STREETS OF ALKALI CITY AS BUCK JONES RODE IN WITH HIS CAPTIVE...

SAY, THE SHERIFF'S BRINGING IN ONE OF CAD SPUR'S MEN!

SHERIFF~~YOU GOT A VISITOR WAITING IN YOUR OFFICE!

SHERIFF'S OFFICE
McGR VE

BUCK'S VISITOR WAS CAPTAIN VEILE OF THE TENTH CAVALRY STATIONED AT FORT WHIPPLE...

THANKS FOR THE TELEGRAPH, SHERIFF. AS IT HAPPENS, BLACK KNIFE LEFT HIS VISITING CARD AT THE MINERS' CAMP ON ARRONDO CREEK TWO HOURS AFTER THE TONTOS BROKE OUT~~FIVE WHITE MEN SCALPED, TEN HORSES MISSING, A HEAP OF STINKING RUINS WHERE THE LOG CABINS USED TO BE~~ I RODE IN TO ASK YOUR HELP...

SURE, CAPTAIN! I'LL JUST LOCK UP THIS HOMBRE~~ THEN I'LL BE WITH YOU!

GRIM-FACED, THE CAVALRY CAPTAIN FOLLOWED BUCK INTO HIS OFFICE.

WELL, CAPTAIN, WHAT CAN I DO FOR YOU?

YOU CAN HELP PUT DOWN A DANGEROUS APACHE RISING, SHERIFF. MOST OF THE TENTH CAVALRY WAS SENT SOUTH FOUR DAYS AGO TO DEAL WITH THE MESCALEROS ON THE PECOS. I'VE BEEN LEFT BEHIND WITH JUST ENOUGH TROOPERS TO GARRISON FORT WHIPPLE, AND NONE TO SPARE FOR HUNTING BLACK KNIFE AND HIS TONTOS! THAT'S WHERE YOU COME IN!

AS CAPTAIN VEILE TURNED GRIMLY AWAY, OLD VIRGIL SALT STEPPED TO HIS SIDE...

I'D LIKE TO HELP YOU, CAPTAIN, SURE I WOULD, BUT MY FIRST JOB IS TO ROUND UP THOSE RUSTLERS AND THAT MAY TAKE DAYS. I GUESS YOU'LL HAVE TO FIND SOMEONE ELSE TO NAIL BLACK KNIFE FOR YOU!

OKAY, SHERIFF. IF THAT'S THE WAY IT IS...

SAY, CAPTAIN, MIND IF I STEP A-WAYS WITH YOU? BE SEEING YOU, BUCK!

THERE WAS A NEW AND PURPOSEFUL GLEAM IN THE FADED EYES OF OLD VIRGIL SALT AS HE FOLLOWED CAPTAIN VEILE INTO THE STREET...

YOU MEAN YOU'VE TANGLED WITH INDIANS BEFORE, MISTER SALT?

HAVE I TANGLED WITH THEM ~~ LOOKIT HERE, CAPTAIN, I SCOUTED FOR GENERAL DAVIS IN THE LAVA BED WAR WITH THE MODOCS ~~ GOT A CITATION HERE FROM THE PRES-I-DENT TO PROVE IT...

BUCK JONES WAS A LAWMAN FIRST AND FOREMOST. HE MUST GO TO THE HELP OF HIS OLD FRIEND~~ BUT NOT BEFORE HE HAD CLEANED UP THE RUSTLERS WHO INFESTED HIS TERRITORY. FIRST HE WENT TO THE ALAMO SALOON...

CAD SPUR AND HIS MEN ARE HOLED-UP IN CRAZY HORSE CANYON, BOYS. HOW LONG WILL IT TAKE YOU TO GET A POSSE TOGETHER?

A DAY I GUESS, SHERIFF, PERHAPS TWO! YOU'LL WANT TWENTY MEN AT YOUR BACK TO BRING IN THOSE RUSTLERS, AND WE'VE GOT TO COLLECT THE BOYS FROM THEIR OUTFITS ALL OVER!

BUCK JONES TURNED GRIMLY AWAY. IF HE WAITED TWO DAYS, AN OLD FRONTIERSMAN MIGHT REACH THE END OF THE TRAIL, WITH AN APACHE ARROW BETWEEN HIS SHOULDER BLADES.

THAT'S WHAT I THOUGHT, CLEM! WAAL, I HAVEN'T GOT TWO DAYS TO SPARE, AND I GUESS I'LL HAVE TO DO WITHOUT THE TWENTY MEN. I'VE GOT TO BRING IN THE SPUR GANG BY SUNDOWN ~~ AND IF YOU CAN'T HUSTLE UP THE POSSE, I'LL HAVE TO DO IT ALONE...

THE SHERIFF WENT BACK TO HIS OFFICE~~ AND HIS PRISONER...

OKAY, NAGLE~~ NOW THE NECKERCHIEF AND STETSON!

I DON'T GET IT, SHERIFF~~BUT IF YOU'RE GOING TO SPEAK UP FOR ME AT MY TRIAL, I'M EASY...

DRESSED IN DAVE NAGLE'S SHIRT AND STETSON, BUCK JONES STALKED GRIMLY OUT OF HIS OFFICE. HE BUCKLED ON HIS GUNS...

HEY, FELLERS, THE SHERIFF'S GOING OUT ALONE IN BROAD DAYLIGHT TO BRING IN THE SPUR BOYS!

WHAT'S THE TARNATION HURRY FOR, ANYWAY, SHERIFF?

I'VE GOT SOME PRIVATE BUSINESS TO ATTEND TO, CLEM~~ AND THE SOONER I DEAL WITH CAD SPUR, THE SOONER I CAN GET ON WITH IT...

Chapter 3 — LONE ROUND-UP

FOUR HOURS LATER, ON THE ROCKY HEIGHTS ABOVE CRAZY HORSE CANYON ~~ ONE OF CAD SPUR'S LOOK-OUTS RAISED HIS RIFLE WITH NARROWING EYES ~~ AND LOWERED IT AGAIN...

SHUCKS, IT'S ONLY DAVE NAGLE! I WONDER WHERE HE'S BEEN SINCE SUN-UP?

SHERIFF BUCK JONES HAD NO TIME TO SPARE FOR A CAREFUL APPROACH TO CAD SPUR'S HIDEOUT. HE RODE STRAIGHT IN WITH HIS GUNS AT HIS HIP ~~ AND~~ DAVE NAGLE'S SHIRT ON HIS BACK...

OKAY, CAD~~ IT'S ONLY DAVE...

BUCK'S RUSE HAD TAKEN HIM INTO THE HEART OF CAD SPUR'S GUARDED HIDEOUT IN BROAD DAYLIGHT~~FROM NOW ON, HIS GUNS WOULD HAVE TO DO THE TALKING...

CLEM SANGSTER'S STEERS ~~THE APACHE PONIES~~ THIS IS WHERE YOU PAY THE RECKONING, SPUR...

STIFF-LEGGED AND GRIM, BUCK JONES STALKED TOWARDS THE CABIN. WITH A KICK OF HIS SPURRED BOOT, HE BURST OPEN THE DOOR. IT WAS THE VIOLENT BEGINNING OF THE SWIFTEST MASS ARREST THAT BUCK JONES EVER MADE...

OKAY, SPUR ~~ I'M TAKING YOU IN...

THIS WAS THE FIGHTING SHERIFF WHO HAD BROUGHT LAW AT THE POINT OF HIS GUN TO SIX WILD COUNTIES ~~ AND THIS TIME HE WAS IN A HURRY...

IT WAS SIXTY SECONDS SINCE SHERIFF BUCK JONES HAD KICKED OPEN THE DOOR OF THE CABIN ~~ THE LAST SIXTY SECONDS OF FREEDOM FOR THE NOTORIOUS SPUR GANG ...

OKAY, SPUR, YOUR BOYS HAVE HAD THEIR FUN ~~ I WANT THEM OUTSIDE, PRONTO, OR THEY'RE GOING TO LOSE THEIR BOSS!

DO AS HE SAYS, MEN ~~ HURRY ~~ DON'T KILL ME, SHERIFF...

BUCK'S VOICE WAS AS HARD AS THE BARREL OF THE GUN WHICH MENACED CAD SPUR'S TREMBLING BACK...

GET MOVING, RATS! I'VE WASTED ENOUGH TIME ON ON YOU, AND NO TRICKS, OR THIS GUN'S LIABLE TO GO OFF...

MOVE, YOU FOOLS! DO YOU WANT TO SEE ME SHOT?

AS THE SULLEN CAVALCADE HEADED ALONG THE CANYON, BUCK ORDERED CAD SPUR TO CALL IN HIS LOOK-OUT. THE LAST OF THE RUSTLERS RODE SLACK-JAWED INTO THE SHERIFF'S NET...

HECK, WHAT HAPPENED...

SHUT UP, CLINT, AND GET INTO LINE! NO ONE AIN'T ARGUING WITH THIS SHERIFF!

MEANWHILE, BACK IN ALKALI CITY, THE RANCH FOREMAN, CLEM SANGSTER, HAD GOT TOGETHER AS MANY MEN AS HE COULD AT SHORT NOTICE. WITH THIS SMALL POSSE, HE WAS RIDING TOWARDS CRAZY HORSE CANYON IN A DESPERATE ATTEMPT TO SAVE HIS SHERIFF FROM AN UGLY FATE...

SAY, CLEM, I SEE HOOF-DUST AHEAD!

IT'S THE SPUR BOYS, I'LL BET! I TOLD THE SHERIFF HE DIDN'T HAVE A CHANCE! WHY, THERE'S SIX OF US HERE, AND THAT AIN'T NEAR ENOUGH TO TACKLE THOSE TEN TOUGH HOMBRES! WE'D BEST TAKE COVER, MEN...

FROM BEHIND ROCKS AT THE SIDE OF THE TRAIL, THE POSSE WATCHED THE APPROACH OF THE NOTORIOUS SPUR GANG WITH COCKED GUNS ~~ AND POPPING EYES...

HECK~~ LOOK!

IT'S THE SHERIFF ~~ AND HE'S BRINGING THEM IN SINGLE-HANDED...

HOWDY, CLEM! I SURE AM OBLIGED TO YOU FOR COMING AFTER ME ~~ YOU CAN TAKE THESE RATS OFF MY HANDS!

EVEN AS THE SULLEN RUSTLERS HALTED UNDER THE GUNS OF THE POSSE, BUCK JONES WAS TURNING HIS HORSE TOWARDS THE OPEN DESERT...

LOCK 'EM UP GOOD AND SAFE, BOYS! YOU'LL FIND THE STOLEN BEEVES UP IN THE CANYON! AND LOOK AFTER THOSE TONTO PONIES FOR ME, WILL YOU ~~ I MAY BE NEEDING THEM...

HEY, SHERIFF, DON'T YOU THINK YOU'VE EARNED YOURSELF A HOLIDAY?

THE LAW HAD BEEN UPHELD. THE LAWMAN WAS FREE NOW. FREE TO FOLLOW AN OLD MAN INTO THE DESERT WHERE THE HARSH APACHES LURKED WITH BLOOD ON THEIR TOMAHAWKS...

RECKON I HAVE AT THAT, CLEM! NOW I CAN ATTEND TO THAT PRIVATE BUSINESS OF MINE...

Chapter 4 — CIRCLE OF DEATH

SOMEWHERE OUT IN THE SAVAGE WILDERNESS OF THE TONTO BASIN, BLACK KNIFE'S APACHE BRAVES WERE HIDING, DEADLY AS RATTLESNAKES. SOMEWHERE, OLD VIRGIL SALT WAS LOOKING FOR THEM WITH HIS FADED EYESIGHT AND RUSTY TRIGGER-FINGER. THE SHERIFF'S FACE WAS GRIM AS HE HEADED WESTWARDS. TWO HOURS LATER ...

APACHES ~~ AND IT. LOOKS AS THOUGH THE OLD-TIMER'S FOUND THEM SOONER THAN HE EXPECTED ...

IT WAS A SCOUTING PARTY OF TWENTY TONTO BRAVES DOWN THERE ON THE PLAIN ~~ PART OF BLACK KNIFE'S BAND. THEY WERE RIDING IN A CIRCLE AROUND THE LONE WHITE MAN ~~ AND THEY WERE WHOOPING WITH THE APACHE LUST FOR BLOOD. FIERCELY, BUCK SPURRED HIS HORSE ...

AS HE FLUNG HIMSELF DOWN BESIDE VIRGIL SALT, BUCK FELT A SURGE OF PITY FOR THE VETERAN WHO HAD ONCE BEEN A LUSTY FIGHTER ON A WILD FRONTIER ~~ AND WHO WAS NOW A HUNTED AND HELPLESS OLD MAN...

DON'T WORRY, OLD-TIMER, I'LL SOON HAVE YOU OUT OF THIS!

BUT BUCK JONES NEED NOT HAVE WORRIED~~ THERE WAS NOTHING HELPLESS ABOUT VIRGIL SALT...

WHY, GOL-DARN IT, YOUNG JONES, I DO BELIEVE YOU FOLLOWED ME OUT HERE TO HOLD MY HAND! ME~~ VIRGIL SALT~~ AS WAS SCRAPPING WITH THE MODOCS BEFORE YOU WAS OUT OF SHORT PANTS! SO YOU'LL SOON HAVE ME OUT OF THIS, WILL YOU?

EASY ON, OLD-TIMER!

WITH THE AWL, VIRGIL WORRIED DIAGONAL HOLES THROUGH THE NOSES OF THREE BULLETS.
HE BLEW THE LEAD SHAVINGS OUT OF THE HOLES, WIPED THE DRILLED BULLETS ON HIS
BUCKSKIN JACKET. THEN HE SLAMMED ONE INTO THE BREECH OF HIS RIFLE.

~~ THEN I PUT ONE OF THE BULLETS WITH A HOLE IN IT INTO MY
RIFLE! NOW WATCH THIS, YOUNG JONES, AND MAYBE YOU'LL
LEARN SOMETHING ABOUT FIGHTING INJUNS...

AIMING HIGH, VIRGIL SALT
SENT THE FIRST DRILLED
BULLET OVER THE APACHES'
HEADS~~AND IT SCREAMED
LIKE A BANSHEE AS THE
WIND CAUGHT THE BORED
HOLE IN ITS NOSE. ...

WHAT A
RACKET!

THAT THERE'S
A SQUALLER,
YOUNG JONES!
SCREAMS SOME,
DON'T IT?

AAGH!

THE WEIRD SCREECH OF VIRGIL SALT'S SECOND BULLET RAISED THE HAIR EVEN ON THE SHERIFF'S SCALP. AND THAT EERIE SOUND FINALLY UNNERVED THE APACHES...

THE WHITE-EYES CALL UP THEIR EVIL SPIRITS TO ATTACK US!

THE AIR SCREAMS! LET' US TURN QUICKLY TO TELL BLACK KNIFE, BROTHERS!

VIRGIL SALT HAD ALREADY SLAMMED THE THIRD SQUALLER INTO THE BREECH OF HIS OLD RIFLE ~~ BUT HE HAD NO NEED TO USE IT. THE APACHE BRAVES WERE FLEEING IN TERROR~~AND BUCK JONES WAS WIPING HIS BROW WITH A GRIN...

WELL, I'LL BE DARNED! IT WORKED, VIRGIL!

SURE IT WORKED! INJUNS ARE A SUPERSTITIOUS LOT! BEST WAY TO THROW THEM IS TO HIT THEM WITH SOMETHING THEY AIN'T SEEN NOR HEARD BEFORE! WELL, COME ON ~~ LET'S GRAB OUR HORSES AND TAKE OUT AFTER THEM...

THE TWO HORSES HAD FOUND SHELTER FROM THE BULLETS IN A BUFFALO WALLOW, FIFTY YARDS AWAY. AS THE TWO MEN WALKED TO COLLECT THEM, BUCK JONES LOOKED WITH A TROUBLED FROWN AT THE OLD FRONTIERSMAN...

YOU'RE FIGURING THOSE BRAVES WILL LEAD YOU TO BLACK KNIFE, EH, VIRGIL? KINDA TRICKY JOB YOU'VE TAKEN ON, HUNTING DOWN THAT RATTLESNAKE, ISN'T IT?

SURE IT IS! ANY MAN-SIZE JOB IS TRICKY! ARE YOU SUGGESTING I AIN'T BIG ENOUGH TO HANDLE IT? AND NOW I THINK OF IT, HOW COME YOU FOLLOWED ME OUT HERE? I THOUGHT YOU HAD SOME UNFINISHED BUSINESS WITH THEM RUSTLERS?

THE SHERIFF'S WORDS WERE TACTFUL~~ BUT VIRGIL SALT'S FADED EYES GLOWED WITH SUDDEN PRIDE...

SO I HAD, OLD-TIMER~~ BUT I FINISHED IT! I JUST FIGURED YOU COULD DO WITH SOME HELP WHEN YOU CATCH UP WITH THAT TONTO KILLER!

WELL, YOU FIGURED WRONG, YOUNG FELLER! YOU CAN TAG ALONG IF YOU WANT TO, BUT JUST KEEP OUT OF MY GUN SIGHTS! THIS IS THE FIRST REAL JOB I'VE HAD SINCE THE BUFFALO QUIT KANSAS LAST FALL~~ AND I AIM TO DO IT ON MY LONESOME!

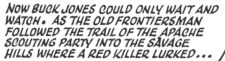

NOW BUCK JONES COULD ONLY WAIT AND WATCH. AS THE OLD FRONTIERSMAN FOLLOWED THE TRAIL OF THE APACHE SCOUTING PARTY INTO THE SAVAGE HILLS WHERE A RED KILLER LURKED...

THEY WATERED THEIR PONIES HERE! SEE THESE FOOTPRINTS ~~ FLAT-BOTTOMED MOCCASINS, TOES TURNED OUTWARDS ~~ TONTO APACHES! AND THEY AIN'T FAR AHEAD, NEITHER...

AT SUNDOWN, THE TWO WHITE MEN WERE THREADING THEIR WAY THROUGH THE FROWNING CANYONS OF WHITE MOUNTAIN. SUDDENLY BUCK LIFTED HIS HEAD, EYES NARROWING WARILY...

WOOD SMOKE DRIFT!

YEP! I RECKON WE'RE PRETTY NEAR BLACK KNIFE'S CAMP! WE'LL REST UP HERE TILL DAWN, YOUNG JONES!

THERE WAS A SUPPRESSED EXCITEMENT IN OLD VIRGIL'S VOICE WHICH WORRIED THE SHERIFF. UNEASILY HE TURNED-IN...

HAVE YOU FIGURED OUT HOW YOU'RE GOING TO TAKE THAT KILLER, OLD TIMER!

I'VE FIGURED, YOUNG JONES! THEM MISGUIDED TONTO BRAVES WILL SOON BE BACK ON THEIR RESERVATION! JUST YOU GRAB SOME SLEEP AND DON'T ROWEL YOURSELF OVER ME AND THAT BLACK KNIFE!

BUCK JONES WAS DOG-TIRED. IN THE LAST TWENTY-FOUR HOURS HE HAD TRACKED THE GANG OF RUSTLERS THROUGH A SLEEPLESS NIGHT ~~ ROUNDED THEM UP SINGLE HANDED ~~ AND TANGLED WITH AN APACHE RAIDING PARTY. SLEEP CAME QUICKLY TO ALKALI CITY'S FIGHTING SHERIFF, AND WHEN IT CAME ...

STEALTHILY, VIRGIL SALT SLIPPED OUT OF HIS BLANKETS AND UNHOBBLED HIS HORSE. HE HAD A JOB TO DO ~~ ALONE ...

NOW I CAN GET MOVING ...

QUIETLY, OLD FELLER ~~ NO SENSE IN WAKING THE SHERIFF ~~ THIS HERE IS OUR PARTY ...

THE MOUNTAIN DARKNESS WAS EDGED WITH ICE, BUT VIRGIL SALT'S THIN OLD BLOOD RAN HOT IN HIS VEINS AS HE URGED HIS HORSE ALONG THE FAINT TRAIL LEFT BY THE TONTO SCOUTS ...

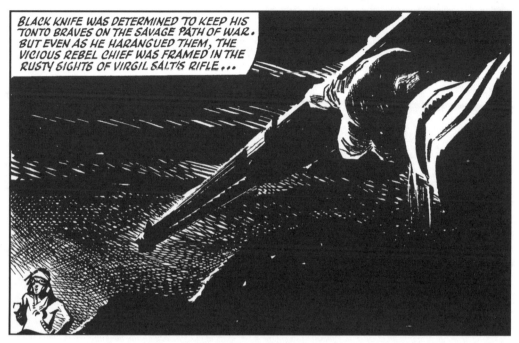

BLACK KNIFE WAS DETERMINED TO KEEP HIS TONTO BRAVES ON THE SAVAGE PATH OF WAR. BUT EVEN AS HE HARANGUED THEM, THE VICIOUS REBEL CHIEF WAS FRAMED IN THE RUSTY SIGHTS OF VIRGIL SALT'S RIFLE...

OLD EYES NARROWED, VIRGIL SALT SQUEEZED THE TRIGGER. THIS TIME THE VETERAN'S AIM WAS DEADLY TRUE ~~ BUT THE BULLET IN HIS RIFLE WAS THE ONE HE HAD LEFT THERE AFTER THE FIGHT IN THE DESERT, EIGHT HOURS BEFORE ~~ A BULLET WITH A HOLE IN ITS NOSE ~~ A BULLET WITH A CROOKED FLIGHT...

GOL-DARN IT! THAT BULLET WAS THE THIRD SQUALLER! I MUST HAVE LEFT IT IN THE BREECH ~~ AND IT'S MISSED BLACK KNIFE BY A MILE!

IT WAS TWENTY SECONDS BEFORE THE OLD FRONTIERSMAN LEVELLED HIS RIFLE AGAIN AT THE FIRELIGHT IN THE GRASSY HOLLOW~~ TWENTY FUMBLING SECONDS TOO LATE...

BLACK KNIFE'S NOT THERE! WHERE THE HECK HAS THAT RATTLESNAKE GONE...

A TWIG SNAPPED SOFTLY BEHIND VIRGIL SALT. SHAKILY HE WHEELED TO FACE THE DEATH STALKING HIM THROUGH THE SHADOWS. AND NOW THE IRON NERVES WHICH HAD LASTED HIM A LIFETIME BEGAN TO FRAY...

THOUGHT I HEARD SOMETHING~~ BUT WHERE — HECK, I'M LOSING MY GRIP...

THE OLD FRONTIERSMAN WAS HELPLESS AT LAST~~ AS BLACK KNIFE SPRANG...

IT SEEMED AS THOUGH VIRGIL SALT HAD REACHED THE END OF A LONG, LONG TRAIL...

YOU HAVE TRIED TO STEAL MY PEOPLE FROM ME, BEARDED ONE! FOR THIS YOU SHALL DIE~~ IN A LITTLE WHILE...

Chapter 5 THE KILLER DIES

MEANWHILE, BACK IN THE CAMP VIRGIL SALT HAD LEFT AN HOUR BEFORE...

WHY, THE STUBBORN OLD FOOL...

WITH GRIM HASTE, SHERIFF BUCK JONES UNHOBBLED HIS HORSE AND LIT OUT AFTER THE OLD FRONTIERSMAN WHO HAD BEEN HIS EARLIEST FRIEND. THE TRAIL WAS STILL FRESH...

GUIDED BY THE SOUND OF HARSH VOICES, BUCK REACHED THE LEDGE FROM WHICH OLD VIRGIL HAD FIRED HIS FATAL SHOT. ONE SWIFT GLANCE TOLD HIM THAT THIS WAS NO TIME FOR SUBTLETY...

NOW THE BEARDED ONE SHALL DIE AT THE HANDS OF BLACK KNIFE. AND THE TONTOS SHALL KNOW THAT WHILE BLACK KNIFE LEADS THEM, THEY ARE INVINCIBLE!

WE WILL FOLLOW BLACK KNIFE, WHO TAMES THE EVIL SPIRITS OF THE AIR!

AMONG THE SAVAGE APACHES IN THE HOLLOW, A HOPELESS OLD MAN PREPARED TO DIE...

YOUNG JONES WAS RIGHT, I'M AN OLD GOAT! I'VE MADE THINGS A SIGHT WORSE BY POKING MY NOSE IN! OUGHT TO HAVE BEEN ROCKING A CHAIR ON A PORCH LONG AGO ~~ BUT I GUESS EVEN A USELESS OLD MAN CAN DIE WELL...

PAINFULLY, THE FADING EYES OF THE OLD FRONTIERSMAN SIGHTED THE BARREL OF THE COLT AGAINST THE PAINTED CHEST OF THE KILLER BEHIND HIM ...

THE CRACK OF THE BLAZING COLT SLAMMED AGAINST THE ROCKY WALLS OF THE CANYON ...

LEAVING THE REJOICING TONTO BRAVES, OLD VIRGIL SALT RODE OVER TO THE THREE MEN WHO WERE WAITING FOR HIM...

MR SALT, YOU'VE DONE A FINE JOB FOR UNCLE SAM ~~ BLACK KNIFE DEAD, THE TONTOS BACK ON THEIR RESERVATION! HOW WOULD YOU LIKE TO CARRY ON THE GOOD WORK ~~ AS INDIAN AGENT TO THE TONTO APACHES?

MY PEOPLE WOULD ESTEEM IT A GREAT HONOUR, O BEARDED ONE!

WHY, SHUCKS...

THE TOUGH FACE OF THE OLD FRONTIERSMAN HAD SOFTENED BRIEFLY. NOW IT WAS FIRM AGAIN ~~ WITH PRIDE...

I CAME TO ARIZONA TO LOOK FOR BUFFALO, BUT I GUESS I FOUND ME SOMETHING A HEAP MORE USEFUL ~~ A PURPOSE IN LIFE!

THERE WAS A GLEAM IN OLD VIRGIL'S EYE AS HE SHOOK HANDS WITH THE SHERIFF OF ALKALI CITY...

WELL, I'VE GOT YOU TO THANK FOR THIS, YOUNG JONES! AND THE LEAST I CAN DO IS TO LEAVE THE FIGHTING TO THEM FAST GUNS OF YOURS IN FUTURE! BUT IF IT'S THE LAST SHOT I EVER TAKE, THAT ONE I BROUGHT BLACK KNIFE DOWN WITH WAS A BEAUTY ~~ DANG ME IF IT WASN'T!

SURE IT WAS, OLD-TIMER! BE SEEING YOU...

CAPTAIN VEILE HAD LISTENED WITH A PUZZLED FROWN TO VIRGIL SALT'S WORDS. NOW, AS HE RODE AWAY BESIDE THE SHERIFF...

I DON'T GET IT, SHERIFF. THE DETACHMENT I SENT TO BRING IN BLACK KNIFE'S BODY REPORTED THAT THERE WAS NO BULLED WOUND ON IT AT ALL!

MAYBE NOT, CAPTAIN! I RECKON IT WAS THE WAY HIS PONY SHIED AT THE GUNSHOT WHICH THREW BLACK KNIFE OFF AND KILLED HIM! THAT LAST BULLET OF OLD VIRGIL'S MISSED BY A MILE...

BUCK JONES GRINNED TO HIMSELF AS HE LOOKED BACK AT HIS OLD FRIEND...

OLD AGE ROBS A MAN OF HIS EYESIGHT, CAPTAIN, BUT IT LEAVES HIM HIS PRIDE. AND THAT'S THE WAY I'M GOING TO LEAVE IT FOR OLD VIRGIL, TOO...

Chapter 1. MAN WITH HATE

THE OLD MAN HAD BEEN PANNING GOLD IN THE RIVER FOR TWO MONTHS. AT FIRST, THINGS HAD GONE QUIETLY. BUT THEN SIGNS HAD BEGUN TO APPEAR...FEATHERS ON THE END OF STICKS... ARROWS STICKING IN HIS MULE'S HARNESS...

...I'D GET UP WITH THE DAWN AND *FIND* THESE THINGS, SON... RIGHT UNDER MY NOSE! IT WUZ THE SAME UP-RIVER WITH OTHERS. A MAN GETS KIND OF EDGY AFTER A WHILE...TOTES A GUN AROUND, AND KEEPS LOOKIN' BEHIND HIM...

IF YOU MEAN TO STAY HERE, TAKE MY ADVICE...*PUT AWAY YOUR RIFLE!*

LATER, ON THE EASTERN TRAIL TO FORT WILLOUGHBY, THE FRONTIERSMAN WEIGHED UP WHAT THE OLD PROSPECTOR HAD SAID...

THERE'S NEVER SMOKE WITHOUT FIRE... IF THE CHEYENNE OR THE SIOUX ARE PLANTING SIGNS, SOMEBODY HAS BEEN STIRRING THEM UP. THAT'S THE WAY INDIAN TROUBLE USUALLY BEGINS!

AT FORT WILLOUGHBY KIT WENT INTO THE COMMANDANT'S OFFICE, EXPECTING TO FIND MAJOR FREEBURG...AND HAD A SURPRISE...

WHERE'S THE MAJOR?

POSTED EAST. THIS IS MY OFFICE...I'M CAPTAIN FOLDMAN, ACTING COMMANDANT OF THIS FORT.

FOLDMAN WAS A STRANGER TO THE FORT. A GHASTLY SCAR RAN DOWN THE LEFT SIDE OF HIS FACE, GIVING HIM AN ODDLY DANGEROUS LOOK. AND THERE WAS ANOTHER ODD THING ABOUT HIM AS A CAVALRY OFFICER...HE ALLOWED A TROOPER SERGEANT TO SPRAWL ON THE EDGE OF HIS DESK...

THE NAME IS CARSON. I RODE IN TO REPORT RUMOURS OF INDIAN TROUBLE!

SAVE IT, CARSON. MR. FOLDMAN AND I, WE GOT OUR OWN TROUBLES, WITHOUT YOURS...

FOR A LONG MOMENT EYES LOCKED . . . THE HARD STEELY APPRAISAL OF THE PLAINSMAN AGAINST THE INSOLENT STARE OF THE CAPTAIN. THEN KIT SWUNG ON HIS HEEL . . .

TOMORROW, CAPTAIN, YOU'LL GET MY WRITTEN REPORT. IT'LL TELL YOU ABOUT THE INDIANS . . . AND A THREAT OF TROUBLE UP-COUNTRY!

YOU CAN BE SURE I'LL READ IT, CARSON . . . WHEN I GET THE TIME!

THINK HE'LL GIVE US TROUBLE, CAPTAIN?

COULD DO, AT THAT COULD BE HE MIGHT FIGURE TO COME BETWEEN ME AND THE INDIANS. I'VE SEEN HIS KIND BEFORE . . . PEACE-MAKERS, WITH BIG HEADS . . .

AS KIT WALKED FROM THE COMMANDANT'S OFFICE, HIS FACE GRIM AND SET, HE WAS HAILED BY BOWLEGS JAKE, OLDEST SCOUT IN THE CHEYENNE TERRITORIES . . .

NOW YOU'VE SEEN FOLDMAN, KIT, I GUESS YOU'VE SEEN EVERYTHING!

THERE WAS LITTLE GOING ON IN THE TERRITORIES THAT OLD BOWLEGS WAS NOT WISE TO... AND KIT WAS SOON LEARNING THE SCORE...

SURE THERE'S INDIAN TROUBLE COMING! HAS BEEN SINCE FOLDMAN ARRIVED. HE'S AFTER INJUN SCALPS, THAT'S WHY... A REAL TROUBLE-SHOOTER!

YOU MEAN THE MAN IS DELIBERATELY STIRRING THINGS UP?

YOU AIN'T HEARD THE HALF OF IT! I CAN TELL STORIES ABOUT THIS CRITTER FOLDMAN FROM AWAY BACK, LONG AFORE HE GOT HIMSELF INTO ARMY UNIFORM...

...YOU'VE SEEN THAT SCAR ON HIS FACE? WELL, HE GOT THAT TEN YEARS AGO. HE WAS A KID AT THE TIME, TURNING TWENTY. HE GOT A JOB AS GUARD WITH A WAGON-TRAIN HEADIN' OUT WEST...

BOWLEGS CONTINUED HIS STORY WHILE KIT CARSON LISTENED INTENTLY...

...THE OTHER INJUNS, THEY SCARPERED OFF WHILE THE GOING WAS GOOD. THE WAGONERS WANTED TO PUNISH FOLDMAN...BUT THEIR LEADER STOPPED THEM. *HE* KNEW THAT NOW THEY WOULD NEED EVERY GUN—EVEN FOLDMAN'S! YOU CAN GUESS, KIT, WHAT HAPPENED TO THAT WAGON-TRAIN!

KNOWING THE CHEYENNE, YES...A DAWN ATTACK, AND MANY SCALPS FOR THE LODGE!

...*THAT'S* JUST WHAT HAPPENED, KIT. NEXT MORNING, THE CHEYENNE STRUCK, AS SOON AS THE WAGON-TRAIN BROKE ITS CIRCLE....

...IT WAS A RUTHLESS MASSACRE. FOLDMAN WAS ONE OF THE LAST TO GO DOWN, FELLED BY A HATCHET BLOW ON THE FACE...

...BUT THE CHEYENNE WERE NOT FINISHED WITH FOLDMAN...FOR HE WUZ STILL ALIVE. STRANGE, AIN'T IT, KIT, THAT HE WUZ THE ONLY CRITTER IN THE WHOLE WAGON-TRAIN TO KEEP HIS SCALP...THE CRITTER WHO CAUSED THE MASSACRE...

WE KILL HIM NOW...HAVE DONE WITH IT.

I SAY WE TAKE HIM TO LODGE, AND KILL HIM SLOWLY!

THE PLAINSMAN, IN HIS DEEP KNOWLEDGE OF MEN, HAD FOUND THE WEAKNESS IN FOLDMAN'S CRUDE ARMOUR...

AND YOU GET THIS, CARSON. *NOBODY'S* GONNA BREAK ME...SEE? I FOUGHT MY WAY UP...I'M HARD AND I DON'T BREAK EASY. THIS GUN HERE... SEE THIS GUN?...*THAT'S* WHAT I RESPECT IT'S MY PEACEMAKER, CARSON. IT'S. BROUGHT *PEACE* TO A LOT OF *ENEMIES* OF MINE...

PUT IT AWAY, AND STOP TALKING LIKE A FOOL.

FROTH HAD BEEN FLECKING FOLDMAN'S MOUTH. THEN SUDDENLY HE HOLSTERED HIS ARMY COLT...TURNED AND WALKED SLOWLY AWAY...

I DON'T SICKEN EASY... BUT I FEEL LIKE I GOT LEAD IN MY STUMMICK. THE MAN'S A RATTLESNAKE!

YES, BOWLEGS. AND IF HE HATES THE INDIANS AS MUCH AS YOU SAY HE DOES, *HOW FAR IS HE GOING TO GO?* HE COULD TURN THE WHOLE OF CHEYENNE TERRITORY INTO A BLOODBATH WITH ONE RIFLE SHOT....AND HE KNOWS IT!

Chapter 2. REVENGE

KIT STAYED AT THE FORT THAT NIGHT, MAKING OUT HIS WRITTEN REPORT. NEXT MORNING, HE WAS AROUND EARLY ENOUGH TO SEE FOLDMAN RIDE OUT AT THE HEAD OF THE REGULAR CAVALRY PATROL. BOWLEGS HAD ALREADY TOLD KIT SOME DISTURBING FACTS ABOUT THESE PATROLS...AND KIT FELT IT WAS TIME HE SAW SOMETHING FOR HIMSELF...

WHERE ARE THEY HEADING FOR?

BORDERLINE OF SIOUX AND CHEYENNE TERRITORY!

THE FRONTIERSMAN GAVE FOLDMAN FIFTEEN MINUTES START...AND THEN HE WAS IN THE SADDLE...

I SAW BUFFALO LAST WEEK, NEAR THE YELLOW SPRINGS... BUT THEY WUZ WELL INTO SIOUX COUNTRY!

IF FOLDMAN KNOWS IT, BOWLEGS, THAT'S PROBABLY WHERE HE'S MAKING FOR. BUFFALO MEANS INDIANS!

KIT CARSON HAD GUESSED FAIRLY CORRECTLY. AT MID-DAY, FOLDMAN WAS LEADING HIS TROOPERS ACROSS HIGH GROUND ABOVE THE YELLOW SPRINGS...

WHAT DO YOU MAKE OF THAT, MISTER FOLDMAN?

TWO INDIAN HUNTING PARTIES AND A LOT OF BUFFALO. NOW SEE WHAT I'M *GOING* TO MAKE OF IT...

ON THE PLAIN, THE TWO INDIAN HUNTING PARTIES, ONE SIOUX, THE OTHER CHEYENNE, WERE MOVING TOWARDS EACH OTHER...

WE ARE NOT ON THE WARPATH.

YET THE SIOUX ARE NOT OUR BROTHERS.

THE LAND IS THEIRS, THE BUFFALO OURS. THERE SHOULD BE TALK, FIRST.

THE NEXT INSTANT, THE SIOUX HAD LEAPT FROM HIS MOUNT AND THE TWO CHIEFS, KNIVES DRAWN, MET IN COMBAT. BOTH PARTIES HUNG BACK, WATCHING IMPASSIVELY...

THEN SUDDENLY IT WAS OVER...SLEEPING HORSE'S OPPONENT SLUMPED TO THE GROUND...

SLEEPING HORSE, HIS WORDS NOW DEEDS WILL WALK TO THE BUFFALO...

AND THEN, FROM THE HILLS, RODE FOLDMAN AND HIS CAVALRY, SURROUNDING THE TWO PARTIES OF INDIANS...

KILL ANY INDIAN THAT TRIES TO RUN, SERGEANT... GRAB THAT MURDERER!

THE PLAINSMAN MOVED IN DELIBERATELY, HOLDING THE EYES OF THE OTHER MAN. HE NOW KNEW, AND SO DID EVERYBODY ELSE, THAT HE WAS FACING A KILLER...

YOU'VE JUST WHIPPED A CHEYENNE CHIEF, FOLDMAN! DO YOU KNOW WHAT THAT MEANS? WAR! THE AVENGING OF THE INSULT WITH BLOOD...THE BLOOD OF EVERY INNOCENT WHITE SETTLER IN THE TERRITORY!

SO I'VE STARTED A WAR. IF I'D STRUNG UP THE INDIAN, AND SHOT HIS MEN, NOBODY WOULD HAVE BEEN *ABLE* TO START A WAR! *YOU* CUT HIM LOOSE, CARSON...

AND THEN KIT'S HAND CLOSED LIKE A VICE ON FOLDMAN'S WRIST AND HE SPOKE QUIETLY...

LISTEN, FOLDMAN. COME TO YOUR SENSES, OR I'LL BREAK YOU AS AN OFFICER *NOW*. THE TROOPERS KNOW ME...THEY'LL TAKE MY ORDERS...

FOLDMAN KNEW THAT HE WAS BEATEN. SUDDENLY, HE BROKE AWAY AND RETURNED HIS GUN TO HIS HOLSTER...

ALL RIGHT, MEN! WE'RE WASTING TIME HERE! SERGEANT, GET YOUR MEN FORMED UP! WE'RE GOING BACK TO FORT WILLOUGHBY!

WITHOUT ANOTHER GLANCE AT THE PLAINSMAN, FOLDMAN CLIMBED INTO THE SADDLE AND THE PATROL MOVED OFF...

ARE YOU DOIN' THE RIGHT THING, CAPTAIN?

LEAVE ME ALONE, AND GET BACK WITH THE MEN.

KIT WATCHED THE CAVALCADE GO, BOWLEGS AT HIS SIDE...

JUST HOW CLOSE TO A RATTLESNAKE CAN A MAN GET ?

THIS IS ONLY THE BEGINNING, BOWLEGS ! EVERY WHITE MAN IN THE TERRITORY WILL PAY FOR WHAT FOLDMAN DID HERE TODAY...

THEN KIT WAS RIDING URGENTLY ACROSS THE YELLOW SPRINGS BORDERLINE, AND INTO THE BADLANDS TO THE NORTH...

I'M GOING TO THE CHEYENNE LODGE ! THE OLDER CHIEFS MAY STILL LISTEN TO ME...

HEAVEN HELP US WHEN WE GET THERE...BUT I'M STILL COMING WITH YOU, KIT !

Chapter 3. WAR WARNING

THE SUN WAS STILL HIGH IN THE SKY WHEN SLEEPING HORSE, THE CHIEF AMONG THE CHEYENNES, RODE INTO HIS LODGE.

SOON, SLEEPING HORSE WAS INCITING HIS BRAVES TO TOTAL WAR...

WE SHALL REPAY INSULT WITH INSULT...DEATH WITH DEATH...BLOOD WITH BLOOD...

BEFORE THE SUN HAD SUNK TO THE MOUNTAIN TOPS, THE CHEYENNE, DAUBED WITH CEREMONIAL PAINT, WERE DANCING THEIR WAR DANCE TO THE QUICKENING THUNDER OF DRUMS...

WHEN KIT CARSON RODE SLOWLY IN, THE WAR FEVER WAS ALREADY STRONG AND GRIM IN THE DRUM-THUDDING AIR...

I DON'T LIKE THIS.., NOT AT ALL!

SAY NOTHING... DO NOTHING. TAKE YOUR LEAD FROM ME...

THEN SUDDENLY, SLEEPING HORSE SWUNG SAVAGELY ROUND . . .

ARE THE WHITE MEN CURS? . . . ARE THEY DOGS WITHOUT HONOUR? . . . THEN LET THEM BRING HE-WITH-THE-SCARRED-FACE, AND HAND HIM OVER TO THE CHEYENNE.

THAT SLEEPING HORSE HAD EVEN SAID ONE WORD WAS A TRIBUTE TO THE FRONTIERSMAN'S STANDING IN THE LODGES OF THE CHEYENNE . . . BUT KIT KNEW THAT SLEEPING HORSE'S PRICE FOR PEACE WAS A PRICE THAT COULD NEVER BE PAID . . .

IT IS NOT IN MY POWER TO BRING YOU THIS MAN.

SLEEPING HORSE HAS SPOKEN.

KIT AND BOWLEGS WERE ESCORTED FROM THE LODGE . . .

AT LEAST WE KNOW WHAT THEY WANT . . . AND WHAT THEY'RE GOING TO DO!

NOTHING WOULD PLEASE ME MORE, AT THIS MINUTE, THAN TO HAND OVER FOLDMAN TO THE CHEYENNE . . .

BY DAWN, THE STOCKADE OF FORT WILLOUGHBY WAS CROWDED WITH SETTLERS... AND THAT WAS HOW FOLDMAN FOUND IT, AS HE WENT TO TAKE OUT A FULL-STRENGTH PATROL...

I'VE NO TIME FOR TALKIN', MA'AM, SO DON'T PESTER ME.

BUT, MISTER FOLDMAN, SURELY WE CAN *REASON* WITH THESE INDIANS...

WITHIN AN HOUR OF DAWN THAT DAY, THE CHEYENNE HAD STRUCK. AN OLD SETTLER, WHO HAD KNOWN THE INDIANS FOR YEARS AND COULD NOT BELIEVE THAT THEY WOULD HARM HIM, STUCK TO HIS HOMESTEAD. WHEN THE CHEYENNE CAME, HE WENT TO MEET THEM WITHOUT A GUN...

THAT SAME DAY, A PRAIRIE SCHOONER HURRYING IN TOWARD FORT WILLOUGHBY FROM THE FAR END OF THE TERRITORY, WAS OVERTAKEN BY SLEEPING HORSE HIMSELF AND HIS WAR PARTY...

IT WAS THE FIRST SIGN OF THINGS TO COME...AFTER THEIR ATTACK, THE CHEYENNE WOULD VANISH LIKE WRAITHS, LEAVING BEHIND THEM ONLY ASHES OR WRECKAGE...

SOMETHING ELSE TO ADD TO FOLDMAN'S ACCOUNT...

NOT MUCH HOPE OF SURVIVORS, KIT...THE INJUNS DO A THOROUGH JOB!

Chapter 4. SLAUGHTER in the CANYON

MUCH INNOCENT BLOOD WAS SPILLED BY THE END OF THE WEEK—AND YET, AS KIT CARSON WARNED, IT WAS ONLY THE PROBING BEFORE THE FULL SCALE ATTACK. FOR THE CAVALRY PATROLS, FOLDMAN OFTEN AT THEIR HEAD, WENT EVERYWHERE THROUGHOUT THE TERRITORY WITHOUT SEEING AN INDIAN...

CAPTAIN, I GUESS THEM INJUNS SCARE EASY AT THE SIGHT OF LONG-KNIVES!

COULD BE. BUT DON'T BANK ON IT.

SOONER OR LATER, THAT FULL SCALE ATTACK WOULD COME. AND IT WOULD BE LAUNCHED AT THE FORT...FOR THE CHEYENNE WERE OUT TO DRIVE EVERY WHITE FROM THE TERRITORY. THIS EVERY SETTLER KNEW AND WITH THE PASSING OF THE DAYS, UNEASINESS GREW...

...AND I SAY IT'S TIME FOR US TO GET OUT. GO EAST, WHILE THE GOING'S GOOD. WE'VE SAVED WHAT WE CAN. LET'S TAKE IT WITH US...WHILE WE CAN!

THERE WAS A GRAIN OF GOOD SENSE IN FOLDMAN'S ATTITUDE--FOR THE FORT WAS THE SAFEST PLACE, AS ALL THE MILITARY MEN KNEW. BUT EVEN WHEN HE WAS TALKING SENSE, FOLDMAN MANAGED TO TWIST IT INTO AN INSULT...

YET YOU WASTE THE TIME OF YOUR TROOPERS ON USELESS PATROLS, FOLDMAN-- EXPOSING THEM TO THE CHEYENNE, INSTEAD OF CONCENTRATING YOUR MEN HERE!

I'VE GOT A *WAR* TO FIGHT, MISTER CARSON... REMEMBER?

THAT DAY, AS FOLDMAN WAS LEADING OUT HIS USUAL PATROL, THE SCHOONERS WERE BEING HARNESSED AND STORED UP...

IF IT'S SETTLED YOU'RE GOING TOMORROW, THEN I WANT ALL THIS STUFF OUT OF HERE AT DAWN! YOU'RE TAKIN' UP USEFUL SPACE!

AND THE SETTLERS, IN THEIR OWN WAY, WERE AS PROUD AND INDEPENDENT AS THE CHEYENNE...

AYE, MISTER FOLDMAN. WE'LL BE OUT OF HERE AT DAWN TOMORROW ALL RIGHT— IF IT'S THE LAST THING WE DO!

THE PATROL WAS HEADING FOR THE BADLANDS, IN THE NORTH OF CHEYENNE COUNTRY...FOR FOLDMAN HAD THE IDEA HE MIGHT TRACK DOWN THE CHEYENNE LODGE THERE, WHILE THE BRAVES WERE AWAY...

I DON'T LIKE SETTLERS, SERGEANT. I DON'T LIKE PEOPLE WHO DIG DIRT, LOOK AFTER COWS. I DON'T LIKE HOMESTEADERS... I DON'T LIKE MINERS...

AND THEN THE CHEYENNE...

ONE MAN, AND ONE ALONE, STABBED RUTHLESSLY BACK TO THE CANYON MOUTH AND FLED WITH TERROR ON HIS HEELS. FOLDMAN'S VILLIANOUS SERGEANT.

AMONG THE SLAUGHTER IN THE CANYON, FOLDMAN WAS DRAGGED FROM HIS HORSE...

LET SCARFACE LIVE— HE IS MINE!

AND SO IT WAS THAT SLEEPING HORSE CAME FACE TO FACE AGAIN WITH THE MAN WHO HAD CAUSED HIS SHAME...

FOR *THIS*, WHITE MAN, I HAVE WAITED LONG! IT IS GOOD YOU ARE STILL ALIVE!

AND FOLDMAN, WHO KNEW HOW THE CHEYENNE DEALT TERRIBLE DEATHS TO THE DESPISED, WAS WEAK AND A COWARD...AND BEGAN TO BABBLE MANY THINGS...

I'LL MAKE A *DEAL* WITH YOU, SLEEPING HORSE...YOU GIVE ME MY *LIFE*, AND I'LL LEAD YOU TO A KILLING... A *REAL COUP*... A WAGON-TRAIN, HUNDREDS OF WHITES, NO LONG-KNIVES...

IT TOOK ALL KIT CARSON'S POWERS OF PERSUASION TO HALT THE *PANICKING* SETTLERS...

...THE *CHEYENNE* WILL BE *EXPECTING* THIS... AND THEY'LL RANGE THE COUNTRY EAST OF HERE. TO GO *NOW,* WITHOUT GUARDS OR PROTECTION, WOULD BE *SUICIDE*...

HOW WE *EVER* GONNA GET PROTECTION, NOW THE TROOPERS ARE GONE?

YEAH, MISTER CARSON... HOW'S *TOMORROW* GONNA BE DIFFERENT FROM *NOW?*

THE PLAINSMAN PURPOSEFULLY PUSHED A WAY THROUGH TO HIS HORSE....

I'LL GET YOU PROTECTION, ALL RIGHT... I'LL GET THE *SIOUX* TO RIDE WITH THE WAGON-TRAIN EAST. THEIR CHIEF WILL LISTEN TO ME...

YOU GONNA GET MORE INDIANS TO HELP US?

TAKING BOWLEGS AND ANOTHER SCOUT ALONG, KIT RACED FROM THE FORT OUT INTO THE DEEP DUSK, HEADING ACROSS THE PLAINS TOWARDS THE YELLOW SPRINGS DIVIDE AND THE SIOUX COUNTRY SOUTH...

Chapter 5. BATTLE for PEACE

THE HARVEST MOON WAS GOLDEN ABOVE THE MOUNTAINS WHEN THE SCOUTS RODE INTO THE LODGE OF YOUNG EAGLE, CHIEF AMONG THE SIOUX...

THE WHITE MAN COMES IN PEACE?

YOUNG EAGLE HAS BEEN MY BROTHER FOR MUCH TIME. HE KNOWS THAT I HAVE ALWAYS COME IN PEACE TO HIS LODGE!

SITTING GRAVELY BY THE FIRE, SMOKING THE PIPE OF FRIENDSHIP AND TAKING HIS TIME IN THE MANNER THE SIOUX EXPECTED, KIT GRADUALLY CAME ROUND TO HIS PURPOSE...

...WE KNOW THAT THERE IS WAR BETWEEN CHEYENNE AND WHITE. WE SIOUX HAVE NO LOVE FOR THE CHEYENNE, BUT THE SCARFACE HAS SHOWN HIMSELF AN EVIL MAN!

HE IS NOW DEAD. MANY WHITES WISH TO LEAVE THE FORT...AND THEY WISH THE BRAVES OF THE SIOUX TO GUARD THEM AGAINST THE CHEYENNE...

BUT THE CHEYENNE, TOO, HAD SET OUT FROM THEIR LODGE AT DAWN...AND THERE WAS A WHITE MAN WITH THEM ALSO...

WHAT SAYS THE WHITE CUR?

HE SAYS THE WAGON TRAIN WILL HAVE NO LONG-KNIVES. WE HAVE KILLED THEM ALL.

THE WAGON-TRAIN HAD BEGUN ROLLING FROM THE FORT WHEN BOWLEGS JAKE, SENT ON AHEAD BY KIT CARSON, CAUGHT UP WITH IT...

THE SIOUX ARE COMING!

I RECKON WE CAN DO WITHOUT THEM. THINGS LOOK LIKE STAYIN' PEACEFUL!

THERE WAS A PLACE WHERE THE EASTERN TRAIL ROSE, FOR A MILE OR TWO, THROUGH ROCKY FOOTHILLS...AND IT WAS HERE THAT SLEEPING HORSE HAD BROUGHT THE CHEYENNE...

THEY COME!

BUT LOOK! THERE ARE MANY MEN AND HORSES AS WELL!

HAS THIS WHITE DOG LIED?

AS THE CHEYENNE MOVED DOWN FROM THE HIGH GROUND, IT WAS A BRAVE WITH EAGLE EYES WHO REALISED WHO THE HORSEMEN WERE...

THEY ARE SIOUX!

THIS CANNOT BE. DO THE SIOUX, THEN, TAKE THE PART OF THE CURS, THE DOGS AND THE FORK-TONGUED?

THE CHEYENNE BORE DOWN ON THE WAGON-TRAIN...AND YOUNG EAGLE AND HIS SIOUX WARRIORS MOVED OUT IN FRONT TO MEET THEM...

I'M GOING OUT THERE WITH THE SIOUX...*GET THE WAGONS IN A CIRCLE!*

THERE WAS, AT THIS TIME, NO WAR BETWEEN CHEYENNE AND SIOUX... AND CHIEF MOVED WARILY FORWARD TO MEET CHIEF...

HAS THE SIOUX BECOME AFRAID, THAT HE RIDES IN PEACE WITH THE WHITE MAN ?

HAS THE CHEYENNE BECOME A MAD DOG, THAT HE BITES WHEREVER HE RUNS ?

...AND INDIAN FELL UPON INDIAN, LIKE STEEL ON STEEL, IN UTTER SAVAGERY, NO MERCY ASKED OR GIVEN...CHEYENNE AGAINST SIOUX, WITH HATCHET, LANCE, AND BOW...

AND SLOWLY, WITH ROCK-HARD STRENGTH, KIT FORCED THE HUGE BRONZE ARM UPWARD AND BACK...UNTIL SUDDENLY, HE HEAVED THE CHEYENNE ON TO HIS BACK.

NO MAN SHALL LIVE WHO *DARES* TO JUDGE ME!

I SHALL... I WHO HAVE JUDGED YOU AND WILL NOW *CONDEMN* YOU, O MAN OF EVIL!

YET THEIR STRENGTH WAS SO EVENLY MATCHED THAT NEITHER COULD MASTER THE OTHER. SWEAT STREAMING FROM THEIR FACES, THEY STRUGGLED...AND THEN, LIKE LIGHTNING, THE PLAINSMAN FLUNG HIMSELF UP AND AWAY. AND, BEFORE THE CHEYENNE COULD FOLLOW...

IT IS OVER, SLEEPING HORSE... THE CHEYENNE HAVE FLED AND THE SIOUX ARE THE MASTERS! I, YOUNG EAGLE, WARN YOU... *MOVE AND YOU DIE!*

THEY TIED HIS HANDS AND DRAGGED HIM INTO THE CIRCLE OF THE WAGONS, AS THOUGH HE WERE AN ANIMAL...FOR HE WAS AN ANIMAL: AN INDIAN CHIEF, ONCE NOBLE, NOW TURNED SAVAGE: A KILLER, WITH THE BLOOD OF THE INNOCENT ON HIS HANDS: THE DEADLY ENEMY, BY HIS OWN VOW, OF THE WHITE MAN, AND NOW THE SIOUX...

THE CHEYENNE SHALL WAR NO MORE...WE, THE SIOUX, HAVE SPOKEN!

WE ARE GRATEFUL, YOUNG EAGLE...AND GLAD THAT THE SIOUX HAVE BROUGHT PEACE!

YET THE MAN WHO, WITH HIS WHIP, HAD TURNED SLEEPING HORSE INTO A RUTHLESS SAVAGE, WAS STILL ALIVE AND UNPUNISHED...

JUST SAY THE WORD, MISTER CARSON...AND WE'LL STRING THIS RAT FOLDMAN UP FROM THE NEAREST TREE! HE SOLD US TO THE CHEYENNE!

CARSON! YOU CAN'T!

HE'LL HAVE TO STAND HIS TRIAL... I KNOW HOW YOU FEEL, ALL OF YOU, BUT THAT'S HOW IT'S GOT TO BE!

AND EVEN THIS ONE STRAW, FLUNG TO HIM BY KIT CARSON, WAS ENOUGH FOR FOLDMAN TO CLING TO...AND HE SWUNG ROUND SNEERINGLY TOWARDS HIS CAPTORS...

I'LL *GET MY TRIAL!* AND WHEN IT'S OVER, AND I COME BACK HERE...

AT THAT MOMENT, SLEEPING HORSE HAD BEEN FORGOTTEN, EVEN BY THE BRAVES WHO HELD HIM CAPTIVE...

IF I DIE, THEN I TAKE WITH ME THE DOG WHO BROUGHT ME SHAME!

AND SO THE WAR OF THE CHEYENNE ENDED...AND PEACE CAME AGAIN TO THE TERRITORY. A NEW AND BETTER COMMANDANT WOULD COME TO FORT WILLOUGHBY...AND THE ANGER AND VIOLENCE WOULD BE FORGOTTEN. THIS KIT CARSON KNEW, AS THE SIOUX AND THEIR CHIEF TOOK THEIR LEAVE OF THE WAGON-TRAIN...

PEACE GO WITH YOU!

AND WITH YOU, YOUNG EAGLE!

AND THE WAGONS STARTED ROLLING AGAIN... BACK TO FORT WILLOUGHBY AND THE HOMESTEADS AND PRAIRIES BEYOND...

THERE'S INJUNS, KIT... AND INJUNS!

THAT GOES FOR THE WHITE MAN, TOO, BOWLEGS! IT'S WHAT'S UNDER THE SKIN THAT MATTERS... AND NEVER FORGET IT!

KANSAS KID *and the*
Brand of the Double-D!

DAN DREW, OWNER OF THE DOUBLE-D RANCH, HAD TAKEN HALF HIS CREW WITH HIM ON A CATTLE DRIVE. THE OTHER HALF WERE OUT ROUNDING UP STRAYS

ONLY THE KANSAS KID, TOP-HAND OF THE DOUBLE-D, REMAINED AT THE RANCH HOUSE AND AS HE STRENGTHENED THE WEAK SPOTS IN THE LONG FENCE AROUND THE HOME CORRAL, HE WAS WONDERING WHERE HE WAS GOING TO FIND THE HIRED HANDS HE NEEDED TO HELP HIM BRAND HIS FINE CROP OF NEW CALVES.

THE THICK-SET HARD-CASE WITH THE BATTERED FACE STOPPED ABRUPTLY IN THE MIDDLE OF A WORD AS THE BIG MAN WHIRLED SUDDENLY. HIS STUBBLED FACE LIVID WITH RAGE...

SHUT YOUR MOUTH, ROSCO!

THE THREE STRANGERS SWUNG THEMSELVES BACK UPON THEIR HORSES AND THE BIG MAN LOOKED OUT OVER THE CORRAL, HIS SLITTED EYES RAKING THE HERD OF LONG-HORN COWS WITH THEIR GOOD CROP OF UNBRANDED CALVES..

OBLIGED FOR THE WATER, MISTER. THIS THE WAY TO CACTUS CITY?

THAT'S RIGHT, FRIEND. YOU'LL HIT TOWN ABOUT SIX MILES DOWN!

THE KID WATCHED THEM THOUGHTFULLY UNTIL THEY WERE OUT OF SIGHT. BUT HE HAD OTHER THINGS TO THINK OF THE DOGIES WERE EATING THEIR HEADS OFF IN THE CORRAL AND HIS STOCKS OF FODDER WERE RUNNING LOW. BUT UNTIL HE COULD GET THE DOUBLE-D BRAND ON THE CALVES HE WAS LOTH TO LOOSE THEM ON THE OPEN RANGE...

NOT CONTENT WITH THE RAKE-OFF HE GOT FROM HIS GAMBLING TABLES, SILAS HICKEY HAD TRIED EVERY TRICK HE KNEW TO CLOSE DOWN HONEST JOHN'S HOTEL.

KANSAS HAD RIDDEN TO THE COUNTY SEAT AND LEGALLY REGISTERED HONEST JOHN'S DEEDS TO THE SECTION OF LAND ON WHICH THE GOOD FORTUNE WAS BUILT, AND HAD SUCCESSFULLY FOILED HICKEY'S RASCALLY ATTEMPT TO FORCE THE HOTEL KEEPER OUT OF BUSINESS. BUT HICKEY HAD SWORN TO GET EVEN.

A FEW MINUTES LATER, THE KANSAS KID WAS CROUCHED OVER LUCKY'S STREAMING MANE AS THE BIG STALLION THUNDERED DOWN THE TRAIL TO CACTUS CITY.

BUT KANSAS WAS WRONG IN THINKING THAT THE THREE MYSTERY RIDERS WERE ENGAGED SOMEHOW IN WRECKING HONEST JOHN'S PLACE. THEY WERE SITTING THEIR HORSES BEHIND A ROCKY BUTTE, NOT MUCH MORE THAN A MILE FROM THE DOUBLE-D.

THERE HE GOES--JUST LIKE HICKEY SAID HE WOULD.

SO ALL WE GOT TO DO NOW IS GO HELP OURSELVES TO ALL HIS UNBRANDED STOCK

LET'S GO!

AT THE UNGUARDED DOUBLE-D RANCH THE THREE RIDERS WORKED FAST AND SKILFULLY. THEY BUNCHED THE LOWING CALVES UP TOGETHER AND DROVE THEM OFF AT A RUN, UP OVER THE RISE AND AWAY.

MUST HAVE BEEN AS EASY AS FALLING OFF A LOG. FIRST THEY GET ME OUT OF THE WAY—AND THEN THEY RUN OFF EVERY LAST ONE OF MY UNBRANDED CALVES! THEY'VE BEEN MIGHTY SMART SO FAR—*BUT I WONDER IF THEY'LL BE SO SMART WHEN I CATCH UP WITH 'EM!*

THE KID WAS ABLE TO FOLLOW THE BROAD TRAIL OF THE STOLEN CALVES WITHOUT DIFFICULTY. IT LED HIM EIGHT MILES SOUTH OF THE DOUBLE-D AND ONTO A BARREN SECTION OF LAND OWNED, HE REMEMBERED, BY NONE OTHER THAN SILAS HICKEY.

THE BIG COWBOY'S LIPS PURSED IN A GRIM SMILE AS HE RECOGNISED THE OLD TUMBLEDOWN LINE-CABIN NEAR THE LONG BOX CANYON AHEAD, AND SAW THE THIN-COLUMN OF SMOKE RISE UP FROM A COOKING FIRE.

STAY RIGHT HERE, LUCKY. I'M GOING TO HAVE A LOOK ROUND!

THE KID CREPT UNSEEN TO THE SIDE OF THE CRUMBLING LINE CABIN AND SAW A CORRAL IN THE CANYON FILLED WITH CALVES.

THERE'S THE MISSING DOUBLE-D STOCK, SURE ENOUGH!

AND SLOWLY, VERY SLOWLY, KANSAS BEGAN TO MOVE AROUND THE CORNER TO THE COOKING FIRE ON THE OTHER SIDE OF THE CABIN.

THE CHINK OF A SPUR GAVE THE KID AWAY, AND THE TWO MEN AT THE FIRE WHIRLED SHARPLY. KANSAS RECOGNISED THEM AS TWO OF THE MEN WHO HAD PASSED THE DOUBLE-D EARLIER IN THE DAY.

I SEE YOU BUTCHERED ONE OF THE CALVES YOU STOLE TODAY. THAT'LL BE ELEVEN DOLLARS. I'LL TAKE IT NOW!

BUT THERE WAS STILL PLENTY OF FIGHT LEFT IN ROSCO.

TAKE ANOTHER LOOK AT THEM CALVES, MISTER. NARY A SINGLE BRAND ON ANY ONE OF 'EM! YOU JUST *PROVE* THEY WAS RUSTLED, AND WE'LL TELL YOU HOW COME!

WE JUST NEWLY DROVE THEM CALVES UP OUT OF EL PIMENTO, FOR SALE TO A FELLER NAME OF SILAS HICKEY.

I WAS JUST WONDERING WHEN MR. HICKEY WOULD BE BROUGHT INTO IT. SO THAT'S THE STORY.

THAT'S THE STORY! AND WHAT DO YOU INTEND TO DO ABOUT IT?

THE KID'S EYES NARROWED.

I AIM TO DO PLENTY! AND FOR A START YOU TWO CAN DRIVE THOSE DOGIES TO THE DOUBLE-D RANCH. COME ON-- GET MOVING, IF YOU KNOW WHAT'S GOOD FOR YOU!

THE KID'S BIG BLACK STALLION SEEMED TO EAT THE MILES, AND SLOWED TO A WALK IN THE MAIN STREET OF CACTUS CITY BARELY HALF AN HOUR LATER.

THIS IS AS FAR AS WE GO, LUCKY——THE WAGGON WHEEL!

SALOON WAGGON WHEEL

THE PUDGY SALOON KEEPER MUSTERED A SICKLY GRIN AS KANSAS STRODE IN.

WHY— IF IT AIN'T THE KANSAS KID. COME ON THROUGH TO THE BAR. HAVE A DRINK ON THE HOUSE.

FORGET IT, HICKEY. I'M NOT HERE ON A SOCIAL VISIT.

THE KID'S GRIN BROADENED.

IN THE BOX CANYON UP BY THE LAZY-Z LINE CABIN. COUPLE OF HOMBRES RAN OFF WHEN THEY SAW ME RUN UP— I RECKON THEY MUST HAVE STOLEN THE HERD —

STOLEN NOTHING! THAT WAS THE HERD I JUST BOUGHT—AND I'VE GOT A BILL OF SALE TO PROVE IT. COME IN AND MEET THE MAN I BOUGHT 'EM FROM!

FOLLOWED BY THE KANSAS KID, HICKEY PUSHED HIS WAY THROUGH THE THRONG OF PEOPLE IN THE BAR, HE STOPPED BY A HUGE MAN WHOM THE KID RECOGNISED AT ONCE. IT WAS THE LEADER OF THE TRIO OF STRANGERS — CHET RAWSON.

CHET— TELL THIS FELLER ABOUT THAT CATTLE DEAL WE DID TODAY, AND WHERE YOU LEFT THE CALVES I BOUGHT.

SURE. THERE WAS A HUNDRED AND TWENTY HEAD OF UNBRANDED CALVES. WE DROVE 'EM UP OUT OF EL PIMENTO. LEFT 'EM IN A BOX CANYON NEAR AN OLD LINE CABIN.

THE KID'S LEFT HAND LEAPED UP QUICKER THAN THE EYE COULD FOLLOW AND THE GLEAMING BARREL OF HIS SIX-SHOOTER SLAPPED WITH BONE-CRUNCHING FORCE AGAINST CHET'S RIGHT GUN-ARM.

CHET GASPED WITH PAIN AND DISBELIEF. THEN HIS GASP TURNED TO A GRUNT OF AGONY AS THE KID'S FIST FLASHED UPWARDS TO SLAM HARD ON THE POINT OF HIS STUBBLED CHIN.

UGH!

HIS COARSE FACE A MASK OF FEAR, RAWSON BACKED AWAY DOWN THE BAR.

HOLD IT, MISTER! I GOT NO QUARREL WITH YOU! I'LL TELL YOU THE TRUTH—HICKEY HIRED ME AND MY PARDS TO RUN OFF THEM CALVES FROM THE DOUBLE-D! HE——

THAT'S WHAT I WANTED TO HEAR. NOW I'LL TAKE THAT FAKE BILL OF SALE, HICKEY!

WHITE WITH RAGE, THE PUDGY CROOK REACHED FOR AN INSIDE POCKET.

YOU WIN, KANSAS. I RECKON YOU ALWAYS—— AAAARRGGGHH!

HIS SNARL TURNED INTO A WAIL OF CHOKING TERROR AS THE KID'S BIG HAND SHOT OUT TO CLOSE LIKE A STEEL VICE OVER HIS FAT WRIST.

THE LITTLE DERRINGER PISTOL HICKEY WAS DRAGGING UP OUT OF A SHOULDER HOLSTER BOOMED LOUD IN THE HUSHED SALOON, AND THE HEAVY SLUG PLOUGHED A SPLINTERING FURROW IN THE ROUGH FLOORBOARDS.

DROP IT!

THE KID HELD THE SCREECHING HICKEY JUST LONG ENOUGH TO REACH INTO THE TWISTER'S POCKET WITH HIS FREE HAND AND PLUCK OUT THE FAKE BILL OF SALE.

THE KANSAS KID REACHED THE SLIP OF PAPER UP TO THE GLASS CHIMNEY OF ONE OF THE SALOON LAMPS, AND GRINNED AS THE NOTE CAUGHT FIRE.

HICKEY! THE NEXT TIME YOU BRING CROOKS INTO TOWN WILL BE THE LAST. AND NO MORE TRICKS LIKE TRYING TO PUT HONEST JOHN OR THE DOUBLE-D OUT OF BUSINESS. REMEMBER, HICKEY— THE NEXT TIME I WON'T BE SO SOFT WITH YOU!

THE KANSAS KID ENDED THAT BUSY DAY AS HE HAD BEGUN IT—IN THE HOME CORRAL OF THE DOUBLE-D. BUT HE WAS NO LONGER ALONE. WITH HIM WERE CHET RAWSON, JUD AND ROSCO—ALL UNWILLINGLY AT WORK...

JUST ANOTHER SCORE OF CALVES TO BRAND AND YOU THREE CAN HIT THE TRAIL FOR GOOD. I SURE HAVE TO THANK SILAS HICKEY FOR FINDING ME THE HIRED HANDS I NEEDED!

BUCK JONES *and the* MAN *from* MONTANA

Chapter 1. DEFIANT SON

IN THE LUSH STATE OF MONTANA, SWAIN BRADLEY HELD COURT—A RANCHER WHOSE BRAND WAS HIS CROWN—WHOSE KINGDOM WAS THE VASTNESS OF BRADLEY COUNTY— WHOSE SUBJECTS WERE THE COUNTLESS CATTLE ROAMING HIS VAST DOMAIN AND THE SCORES OF MEN WHO TENDED THEM.

THE SHRILL WHINNYING OF DESPERATE HORSES, THE MUFFLED GRUNTS OF TANNED YOUNG HORSE-BREAKERS—THESE SOUNDS SURGED THROUGH THE DRIFT OF SUN-BAKED DUST WHICH SWIRLED ABOUT THE HOME CORRAL OF SWAIN BRADLEY'S RANCH...

THAT THERE'S A SON TO BE PROUD OF, MR. BRADLEY—A REAL TOP-NOTCH COWBOY IF EVER THERE WAS ONE!

ACCURATELY PUT, LOMAX. HE HAS THE SPIRIT AND THE CAPABILITIES WHICH HAVE MARKED OUR FAMILY FOR MANY GENERATIONS.

THE STALLION BUCK-JUMPED THE LENGTH OF THE CORRAL AND BACK AGAIN. FINALLY, HE WAS BROKEN AND, SMILING LIGHTLY, YOUNG JEFF BRADLEY SWUNG HIMSELF FROM THE SADDLE...

THAT'S ENOUGH FOR TODAY. I'LL BREAK THE REST OF THEM TOMORROW. WHEW! WHY DON'T WE GET BROKEN HORSES DELIVERED DURING THE COLD WEATHER?

SWAIN BRADLEY MADE AS IF TO ANSWER, BUT A COMMOTION BEHIND HIM BROUGHT HIM WHIRLING ROUND ON HIS HEEL...

HEY, BOSS! I'VE CAUGHT US A REAL LIVE SHEEPMAN!

A SHEEPMAN! BY GLORY, YOU'D BETTER HAVE A GOOD REASON FOR DRAGGING HIS MANGY CARCASS ON TO MY RANCH!

WE FOUND HIM ON YOUR LAND... SAID SOME OF HIS SHEEP HAD GONE ASTRAY!

FOR NEARLY A YEAR, SINCE SHEEP RANCHERS HAD FIRST MOVED INTO MONTANA, BITTER FEUDS HAD RAGED BETWEEN THEM AND THE CATTLEMEN WHO CLAIMED THAT THE SHARP-FOOTED SHEEP DESTROYED THE LUSH PRAIRIE GRASS. LEADERSHIP OF THE CATTLE FACTION HAD NATURALLY FALLEN TO SWAIN BRADLEY, WHO HAD TAKEN A SADISTIC INTEREST FROM THE START.

I'M GLAD MY MAN DID NOT KILL YOU, SCUM! YOU'LL TAKE A MESSAGE BACK TO YOUR STINKING, DIRT-GRUBBING KIND...

DON'T WASTE YOUR WORDS ON HIM, MISTER BRADLEY. *I'LL* FIX HIM UP WITH A MESSAGE!

IN THE SPACE OF A SECOND IT WAS ALL OVER! JEFF BRADLEY'S HAND DROPPED TO HIS HIP TO COME UP FULL OF BUCKING FORTY-FIVE BEFORE HIS ANTAGONIST'S TRIGGER FINGER HAD EVEN BEGUN TO TIGHTEN!

IN THE SUDDEN SILENCE WHICH FOLLOWED THE STUNNING CRESCENDO OF SHOTS, JEFF BRADLEY CUT THE SHEEPMAN LOOSE AND LIFTED HIM ON TO THE COWHAND'S HORSE. THEN HE STRODE TO HIS OWN MOUNT AND SWUNG HIMSELF INTO THE SADDLE...

I'M GOING, FATHER—AND I WON'T BE BACK. BUT YOU'LL HEAR FROM ME—I PROMISE. *YOU'LL HEAR FROM ME!*

Chapter 2. PRAIRIE BATTLE

FAR TO THE SOUTH, IN ARIZONA, ALKALI CITY WAS ALIVE WITH EXCITEMENT! LONG STREAMERS OF BUNTING FLUTTERED THE LENGTH AND BREADTH OF MAIN STREET, AND A HUNDRED PAINT BRUSHES SLAPPED A NEW AND BRILLIANT SURFACE ON ALL THE SHOPS AND SALOONS... ALKALI CITY WAS PREPARING FOR THE ANNUAL ARIZONA RODEO!

HOW ARE YOUR BOYS PLACED FOR THE RODEO, RUBE? DO YOU FIGURE TO SWEEP THE BOARD?

SHUCKS, BUCK I AIN'T ONE FOR BRAGGIN', YOU KNOW THAT, BUT I RECKON WE'LL GET THOSE CUPS SURE ENOUGH!

THE TWO MEN STARED SILENTLY AT EACH OTHER. THEN THE FIGHTING SHERIFF TURNED ABRUPTLY AND STRODE AWAY...

THAT STUPID YOUNG FOOL'S GOING TO START A RANGE WAR, OR MY NAME'S NOT BUCK JONES... *BUT HOW AM I GOING TO STOP HIM?*

ONLY FOUR DAYS LATER, THE TROUBLE BEGAN. A TRAVEL-STAINED RIDER THREW HIMSELF FROM A SWEATING HORSE AT THE DOOR OF BUCK'S OFFICE...

SHERIFF! THERE'S A RING O' FLYIN' DIAMOND BOYS AROUND THAT SHEEPMAN'S SPREAD——AN' BOY, I RECKON THEY ARE JUST ABOUT READY TO DO SOME ROPE STRETCHIN'!

RACING OUT OF HIS OFFICE, BUCK LEAPT INTO THE SADDLE OF HIS STALLION, AND SILVER'S HOOFS WERE SOON PUTTING ALKALI CITY WELL BEHIND...

MEANWHILE, OUTSIDE JEFF BRADLEY'S RANCH-HOUSE THE SCENE WAS ONE OF MENACE...

COME OUT, BRADLEY, WE WANT TO TALK TO YOU—— AN' YOU'D BETTER LISTEN TO WHAT WE SAY!

FOR A MOMENT THERE WAS NO REPLY, THEN A PUFF OF WHITE SMOKE BLOSSOMED AT A WINDOW, AND A HEAVY SLUG RIPPED THE DUST AT RUBE TOOMEY'S FEET!

AAAAGH!

OMINOUSLY, TOOMEY THUMBED BACK THE HAMMER OF HIS FORTY-FIVE AS HE REGAINED HIS BALANCE...

ALL RIGHT, BRADLEY! YOU ASKED FOR IT! WE'RE COMIN' IN THERE——SO GET READY TO DIE!

ONLY FOR A MOMENT DID BUCK NEED TO THINK...

OF COURSE! THAT RIVER RUNS ACROSS JEFF BRADLEY'S RANCH! THIS IS ANOTHER OF RUBE TOOMEY'S TRICKS!

SOON, BUCK WAS RIDING ALONG THE RAPIDLY DRYING WATERCOURSE. UP IN THE HILLS, WAY BEYOND THE FLYING DIAMOND SPREAD, HE FOUND THE RIVER DIVERTED—ITS NATURAL COURSE BLOCKED BY WHAT SEEMED TO BE AN ORDINARY ROCKSLIDE...

SO! MAYBE RUBE DIDN'T HAVE ANYTHING TO DO WITH THIS!

BUT THEN, AS HE EXAMINED THE DAM, HE FOUND SOMETHING WHICH BROUGHT A GLEAM OF INTEREST TO HIS EYE. WITHOUT SEARCHING FURTHER, HE RODE STRAIGHT TO THE FLYING DIAMOND RANCH...

WHY, BUCK! WHAT BRINGS YOU HERE?

CUT THE PLEASANTRIES, RUBE. YOU KNOW WHY I'VE COME.

RUBE TOOMEY FEIGNED INDIGNANT SURPRISE, UNTIL BUCK PRODUCED A FRAGMENT OF HALF BURNED DYNAMITE FUSE AND THREW IT INTO THE FOREMAN'S HANDS...

UH... WELL, BUCK, I...UH...

YOU'VE SAID ENOUGH, RUBE. I CAN SEE BY YOUR EYES THAT YOU KNOW ALL ABOUT THE RIVER DAM.

I COULD TAKE YOU IN FOR THIS RUBE. BUT I WON'T—NOT IF YOU AND YOUR BOYS COME WITH ME RIGHT NOW AND BLAST THAT DAM APART.

I AIN'T GOT MUCH CHOICE WHEN YOU PUT IT THAT WAY... OKAY, BUT THE BOYS WON'T LIKE IT.

ON THE WAY BACK TO ALKALI, BUCK MET JEFF BRADLEY WORKING ON HIS RANCH...

HOWDY, BRADLEY. YOU MIGHT CARE TO KNOW THAT YOUR WATER IS BACK AGAIN.

IT WOULD HAVE TAKEN MORE THAN THAT TO DRIVE ME OFF. I'M A DETERMINED MAN, SHERIFF, AND I DON'T NEED HELP FROM ANYONE—— EVEN YOU!

YOU'RE A STUBBORN FOOL, BRADLEY. BUT AS SHERIFF, I HAVE TO PREVENT TROUBLE ...AND THAT MEANS LOOKING AFTER YOU WHETHER YOU LIKE IT OR NOT!

TIGHT-LIPPED, BUCK RODE ON, THE BURNING EYES OF JEFF BRADLEY SEARING INTO HIS BACK...

A FOOL, AM I? SHERIFF, YOU HAVE GOT A BIG SURPRISE COMING WHEN THE RODEO STARTS— AND SO HAS MY FATHER!

Chapter 3. THE RODEO

SEVEN DAYS LATER, AFTER A STEADY STREAM OF VISITORS HAD BEEN ARRIVING IN ALKALI FROM ALL OVER ARIZONA, THE HUGE GROUND ON THE EDGE OF TOWN WAS OFFICIALLY DECLARED OPEN, AND THREE THOUSAND SPECTATORS MILLED TO THEIR SEATS ON THE FIRST DAY OF THE GREAT RODEO!

SEVEN MORE ENTRANTS CAME AND WENT, NONE OF THEM ABLE TO BETTER TOOMEY'S EFFORT. THEN CAME THE LAST CONTESTANT – A SURPRISE ENTRY...

AND NOW, FOLKS, AN ENTRANT WHO WANTED HIS NAME KEPT FROM YOU UNTIL THE LAST MINUTE. *GOOD LUCK TO JEFF BRADLEY!*

EXCITED MUTTERINGS RAN THROUGH THE CROWD, FOR THERE WERE FEW–EVEN AMONG THE NEWCOMERS TO ALKALI – WHO HAD NOT HEARD OF THE REBEL RANCHER...

WHAT NERVE! THAT ORNERY SHEEPMAN! WHAT IN HECK DOES HE THINK HE'S PLAYIN' AT!

RUBE TOOMEY AND HIS BOYS COULD ONLY GAPE IN SHEER AMAZEMENT, BUT THERE WERE FURTHER SHOCKS TO COME... THE NEXT EVENT WAS BULL-DOGGING—EASILY WON BY JEFF BRADLEY...

...ALSO THE NEXT EVENT—BRONCO-BUSTING...

AMONG THE REPORTERS WAS LIVE-WIRE JOHNNY DIAMOND... REPRESENTING THE LARGEST ARIZONA PAPER – THE BANNER...

SURELY YOU'VE BEEN A CATTLEMAN TO LEARN ALL THOSE TRICKS? WHAT MADE YOU CHANGE?

THAT ISN'T ARIZONA'S CONCERN. YOU FIND THE ANSWER TO THAT QUESTION IN MONTANA.

SO YOU'RE FROM MONTANA. GOOD! MY PAPER'S GOT A TIE-UP WITH THE SUN SENTINEL UP THERE. ANY OBJECTION IF WE SEND THIS STORY NORTH FOR THEM TO USE?

OBJECTION? NO SIR! I'D HAVE ASKED YOU TO IF YOU HADN'T SUGGESTED IT. BE SURE THE HEADLINE READS WHAT I TOLD YOU THOUGH.

Chapter 4. OUTLAW ARMY

IT WAS A LONG, TIRING JOURNEY FROM ARIZONA TO MONTANA — ONE THAT WOULD HAVE TAKEN MANY DAYS ON HORSEBACK. SO BUCK JONES CHOSE TO LEAVE HIS FAITHFUL SILVER BEHIND, AND CHANGE HIS SADDLE FOR THE COMFORT OF A FIRST-CLASS SEAT ON THE NORTHERN EXPRESS...

INTRODUCING HIMSELF, BUCK QUICKLY EXPLAINED TO THE SURPRISED RANCHER WHY HE HAD COME...

YOUR SON'S CAUSING ME A HEAP OF TROUBLE, MISTER BRADLEY. HE'S OBVIOUSLY A BORN CATTLEMAN, BUT HE'S STARTED A SHEEP-RANCH RIGHT IN MY COUNTY. I WANT TO KNOW HIS REASON FOR DOING IT.

A *SHEEP* RANCH? WHY THE GOLDARNED YOUNG. FOOL!

BUCK SOON HEARD HOW JEFF BRADLEY HAD CHOSEN TO DEFY HIS FATHER AND SUPPORT THE SHEEP FACTION.

BUT WHAT IS HE TRYING TO PROVE?

DON'T WORRY, MISTER BRADLEY. NOW I KNOW HIS REASONS, MAYBE I CAN THINK OF A WAY TO CHANGE HIS MIND. RIGHT NOW, HE'S PUTTING THE PEACE OF MY COUNTY AND HIS OWN LIFE IN DANGER.

WHEN THE SHERIFF HAD LEFT, HALF-A-DOZEN MEN, ALL LAUGHING AND WAVING NEWSPAPERS, BURST INTO THE SALOON...

SHEEPMEN! WHAT THE...?

SCARCELY ABLE TO CONTROL THEIR LAUGHTER, THE SHEEP HERDERS SURROUNDED THE IRATE CATTLE-KING...

HAW! HAW! THAT'S A REAL PIPPER OF A SON YOU'VE GOT, WHERE'S THE FAMILY NAME NOW, BRADLEY?

SHAKING WITH RAGE, SWAIN BRADLEY GRABBED A PAPER AND READ THE ACCOUNT OF HIS SON'S RODEO EXPLOITS...

HE'S MADE ME LOOK THE BIGGEST FOOL IN THE STATE! BY GLORY, HE'LL PAY FOR THIS! *HE'LL PAY ALL RIGHT!*

TRYING TO IGNORE THE TAUNTS OF THE SHEEPMEN, BRADLEY STRODE FROM THE SALOON AND MADE HIS WAY TO A DINGY GAMBLING DEN...

McCOY'S YELL HIT BUCK WITH SUCH IMPACT THAT THE LAWMAN NEVER LIFTED HIS GUNS OUT OF THEIR HOLSTERS...

ARIZONA! NOW WHY ARE THOSE TOUGHS HEADIN SOUTH?

HIS TRAIN FORGOTTEN, BUCK RACED TO THE TOWN LIVERY STABLE AND BORROWED A FAST HORSE...

THEY ARE CERTAIN TO CAMP FOR THE NIGHT. MAYBE I CAN FIND OUT WHAT THEY'RE UP TO.

Chapter 5. NIGHT ATTACK

ANOTHER DAY PASSED BEFORE THE OUTLAWS CROSSED INTO ARIZONA. WHEN THEY NEARED ALKALI CITY, THEY HAILED A PASSING RIDER... IT WAS RUBE TOOMEY OF THE FLYING DIAMOND!

HOLD IT, STRANGER!

A SINGLE GLANCE TOLD TOOMEY THAT THESE RIDERS WERE TOUGH, RUTHLESS MEN...

WHERE CAN WE FIND THE BRADLEY SHEEP SPREAD?

WHAT'S YOUR BUSINESS WITH HIM, MISTER?

NO SOONER HAD THE BANDITS DISAPPEARED, THAN RUBE TOOMEY SWUNG HIS PINTO ROUND AND STREAKED TOWARDS ALKALI CITY...

TO BLAZES WITH BRADLEY, BUT TOUGHS LIKE THAT MOVIN' INTO ARIZONA ISN'T HEALTHY!

AT THAT MOMENT, ONLY FOUR MILES AWAY, THE SOUTHBOUND FLYER FROM MONTANA WAS HALTED AT A WATER STOP.

SAY — IS THIS STOP ANYWHERE NEAR THE BRADLEY SHEEP RANCH? DO YOU KNOW THE PLACE I MEAN?

KNOW IT? EVERYONE IN THE STATE KNOWS IT. YOU CAN SEE THE BOUNDARY FENCE FROM THE WINDOW.

WHEN THE ATTENDANT LEFT, SWAIN BRADLEY STEPPED NERVOUSLY ON TO THE OBSERVATION PLATFORM...

I'LL GO STRAIGHT TO JEFF'S. I'LL ONLY BE WASTING TIME IF I GO INTO ALKALI CITY!

AS THE TRAIN SLOWED AT A STEEP GRADIENT, THE RANCHER LEAPED DOWN AND MADE FOR THE FENCE, KNOWING, BUT NOT CARING, THAT A TOUGH WALK WAS AHEAD OF HIM...

ALL I HAVE TO DO IS TO GET TO JEFF'S PLACE BEFORE SLICK ZARDIS...

MEANWHILE, RUBE TOOMEY WAS MAKING A ROUND OF ALKALI CITY, GATHERING IN HIS OFF-DUTY HANDS...

COME ON, YOU GUYS — DOWN TO THE SHERIFF'S OFFICE! HURRY IT UP!

AND TEN MINUTES LATER, BUCK JONES WAS SURPRISED TO SEE TWELVE FLYING DIAMOND COWBOYS OUTSIDE HIS OFFICE...

WHAT'S THIS, A DEPUTATION?

NO, BUCK — A POSSE! I RAN ACROSS A BIG BUNCH OF MEAN HOMBRES — HEADED FOR BRADLEY'S PLACE! BETTER COME WITH US, BUCK.

THERE WAS A MOMENT'S TENSE SILENCE — AND THEN A BLASTING CRESCENDO OF SHOTS THAT SHATTERED THE NIGHT!

AS THE ECHOES OF THE LAST SHOT FADED, THE HOUSE WAS SILENT—BUT ZARDIS HAD SEEN THE FIGURE INSIDE STAGGER, REEL, AND DROP.

NEATLY DONE, BOYS. DON'T BOTHER ABOUT BUSTING UP THE SPREAD. THERE'S NO NEED FOR THAT NOW!

THERE WAS A SMUG SATISFIED LEER ON SLICK ZARDIS' FACE AS HE THOUGHT OF THE MONEY HE COULD WRING FROM SWAIN BRADLEY – BUT IT WAS A LOOK WHICH QUICKLY VANISHED AT THE SOUND OF HOOFS...

QUICK! WE'VE GOT COMPANY!

AS THE CROOKS FRANTICALLY RELOADED THEIR WEAPONS, BUCK AND THE 'FLYING DIAMOND' POSSE HURTLED INTO THEM

TAKE THAT, YOU MURDERING RAT!

SHOOT 'EM DOWN!

A SPORADIC RATTLE OF GUNFIRE BROKE OUT AS SOME OF THE OWLHOOTERS AT LAST BROUGHT THEIR COLTS INTO ACTION...

EVEN AS THE TWO MEN HIT THE GROUND, THE FIGHTING SHERIFF'S FIST CURLED ROUND IN A LONG, RAKING ARC!

CHEST HEAVING, BUCK STOOD UP AND GLANCED TO WHERE TOOMEY AND HIS MEN HAD SUCCESSFULLY ROUNDED UP THE REST OF THE GANG...

BUT WHEN THE CAVALCADE REACHED ALKALI, A PARALYSING SHOCK AWAITED ZARDIS. AS HE ENTERED THE JAIL, A CELL DOOR OPENED, AND *OUT STEPPED JEFF BRADLEY*, WHOM BUCK HAD LEFT THERE FOR HIS OWN SAFETY.

YOU! AAAAGH! NO, IT CAN'T BE!

I REMEMBER YOU, ZARDIS! SO YOU WERE OUT TO GET ME, WERE YOU?

AT HIS FATHER'S BEDSIDE, JEFF HEARD THE WHOLE STORY...

SO IT WAS *YOU* WHO SET THOSE GUNMEN ON TO ME! YOU... MY OWN FATHER...

BUT NOT TO HARM YOU, SON! I SWEAR IT... ONLY TO BUST UP YOUR SHEEP SPREAD AND MAKE YOU COME BACK TO MONTANA.

JEFF SAW THE MISERY IN HIS FATHER'S EYES... AND REMEMBERED BUCK'S WORDS — "YOU'LL NEED ALL YOUR FORGIVENESS, JEFF"

I... I GUESS WE'VE BOTH ACTED LIKE FOOLS. IT WAS MY FAULT AS MUCH AS YOURS.

WHEN I SAW THAT I'D NEARLY GOT YOU KILLED, I REALISED HOW WRONG I HAD BEEN WITH MY CRAVING FOR POWER. IF YOU'LL COME BACK WITH ME TO OUR RANCH, I'LL PROVE IT!

COWBOY PICTURE LIBRARY

WESTERN SCRAPBOOK

INDIANS NEVER BOTHERED ABOUT THE TASTE OF THEIR FOOD. THEY ATE MERELY BECAUSE THEY WERE HUNGRY, AND THE TASTE, WHETHER PLEASANT OR NASTY MADE NO DIFFERENCE.

WHEN BUFFALO BILL CODY WAS A LAD ABOUT TEN HE USED TO ROUND UP WILD HORSES, BREAK THEM IN AND SELL THEM TO THE SOLDIERS AT FORT LEAVENWORTH FOR TEN DOLLARS EACH.

JIM BRIDGER, THE FAMOUS SCOUT, HAD LITTLE EDUCATION, BUT HE TRADED A YOKE OF CATTLE WORTH 125 DOLLARS FOR A VOLUME OF SHAKESPEARE. HE THEN HIRED A GERMAN BOY AT 40 DOLLARS A MONTH JUST TO READ IT TO HIM: AND EVER AFTER, THE FRONTIERSMAN WENT ABOUT QUOTING SHAKESPEARE.

TOM HORN WAS A NOTED INDIAN SCOUT. HE TURNED A PROFESSIONAL MAN-HUNTER AT ONE STAGE OF HIS CAREER, AND KILLED RUSTLERS FOR SIX DOLLARS A HEAD.

WHEN BUFFALO BILL WAS A YOUNG PONY EXPRESS RIDER, HE ONCE SAW A RUNAWAY STAGECOACH WHOSE DRIVER HAD BEEN KILLED BY PURSUING INDIANS. FIRING AT THE REDSKINS, BILL CODY SPURRED HIS PONY ALONGSIDE THE SWAYING COACH AND LEAPED ABOARD. GRABBING THE REINS, HE CONTROLLED THE TEAM AND GOT THE STAGE WITH ITS GOLD AND PASSENGERS TO SAFETY.

INDIAN SINGING CONSISTED OF THREE OR FOUR UNPLEASANT-SOUNDING GUTTURAL NOTES WHICH FINISHED UP WITH A SHRILL YELL.

THE NAVAJO INDIANS WERE EXPERT BASKET-MAKERS. THEY WOVE WILLOW TWIGS SO CLOSELY AND TIGHTLY THAT THE BASKETS WERE USED FOR CARRYING WATER.

WHEN THE BLACKFEET HAD AN IMPORTANT TRIBAL WAR WITH THEIR ENEMIES, THEY WOULD TAKE ALONG A LUCKY MASCOT, USUALLY AN INDIAN MAIDEN, DRESSED IN WHITE, LEADING A MAGNIFICENT WAR-HORSE. THE HORSE CARRIED A MEDICINE BAG AND A DECORATED WAR-PIPE.

IN THE DAYS WHEN TEXAS WAS A YOUNG STATE, BURK BURNETT, A COWBOY, WON A RANCH IN A CARD GAME. HE CALLED IT THE 6666 AFTER THE POKER HAND OF FOUR SIXES WHICH WON HIM THE PROPERTY AND TURNED HIM INTO A CATTLE BARON.

THE COWBOY SONGS OF THE WEST WERE ALL WRITTEN TO THE RHYTHM OF THE WALK, TROT AND GALLOP OF HORSES.

BELLE STARR, KNOWN AS THE 'OUTLAW QUEEN', ALWAYS USED A .44 CALIBRE SADDLE-RIFLE. ON ONE SIDE OF ITS WALNUT STOCK DONE IN SMALL BRASS TACKS, WAS HER NAME, AND ON THE OTHER SIDE A BELL AND A STAR. ALONG THE EDGE OF THE STOCK SHE HAD CUT SEVEN NOTCHES, ONE FOR EACH MAN SHE HAD KILLED.

MARBLES WAS A GAME PLAYED ONLY BY GIRLS IN THE SIOUX TRIBE — THE BOYS SCORNED IT. THE MARBLES USED WERE LITTLE ROUND, POLISHED PEBBLES OR STONES.

WHEN ON SPECIAL OCCASIONS THE UTE INDIANS SMOKED, THEY DID NOT USE PIPES BUT VERY LARGE CIGARETTES MADE BY ROLLING THEIR TOBACCO - OR WHATEVER ELSE THEY SMOKED - IN PAPER, LEAVES, OR THE INNER BARK OF RED WILLOW TREES.

THE UTE INDIANS, BESIDES BELIEVING IN THE GREAT SPIRIT, ALSO WORSHIPPED THE SUN.

Printed in England and published each month by Fleetway Publications Ltd., Fleetway House. Farringdon Street, London. E.C.4. Sole Agents: Australasia, Messrs. Gordon & Gotch, Ltd.; South Africa, Central News Agency, Ltd.; Federation of Rhodesia and Nyasaland, Messrs. Kingstons, Ltd. COWBOY PICTURE LIBRARY is sold subject to the following conditions, that it shall not, without the written consent of the Publishers first given, be lent, resold, hired out or otherwise disposed of by way of Trade except at the full retail price as shown on the cover; and that it shall not be lent, resold, hired out or otherwise disposed of in a mutilated condition, or in any unauthorised cover by way of Trade: or affixed to or as part of any publication or advertising, literary or pictorial matter whatsoever.
SL

DAVY CROCKETT AND THE
DUEL WITH DANGER!

THIS IS THE STORY OF A LAND UNTAMED—A LAND WHERE SAVAGERY LIVED SIDE BY SIDE WITH CIVILISATION, WHERE MEN FOUGHT HARD AND ENDLESSLY TO KEEP HOLD OF ELUSIVE PEACE... THIS IS THE STORY OF A LAND WHERE THE FORCES OF GOOD AND EVIL WERE AT CONSTANT WAR, AND WHERE EVIL OFTEN TRIUMPHED — UNTIL SOMEONE OF SUPREME BRAVERY, OF MAGNIFICENT EXAMPLE, CAME TO CLOSE THE BREACH — *SOMEONE LIKE DAVY CROCKETT!*

IT HAD TAKEN FOUR YEARS OF TOIL FOR THE HARDY SETTLERS WHO CAME WEST TO THE FERTILE LANDS BEYOND THE MISSOURI, TO TRANSFORM SMALL PATCHES OF THE WILDERNESS INTO OUTCROPS OF CIVILISATION WHERE A MAN COULD LIVE IN COMPARATIVE SECURITY.
SUCH AN OUTPOST WAS CANNON'S CROSSING.
IT WAS ON A QUIET WEEKDAY MORNING THAT CANNON'S CROSSING BECAME THE SCENE OF VIOLENT ACTION — THE DAY A RAGGED, DUSTY RIDER GALLOPED INTO TOWN!

TREACHEROUS, SNEAKIN' VARMINTS!

...BUTCHERY! COLD-BLOODED MASSACRE!

A WHOLE FARMSTEAD WIPED OUT BY THE RED DEVILS!

AN OUTLYING HOMESTEAD HAD BEEN ATTACKED, PLUNDERED, AND UTTERLY DESTROYED BY A BAND OF REDSKIN RAIDERS...

WHAT WERE THEY? CHOCTAWS? OSAGE? SHASTA?

HOW I ESCAPED WITH MY LIFE, I SHALL NEVER KNOW!

WHAT IN GLORY DOES IT MATTER? THEY'RE ALL A BUNCH OF COWARDLY HEATHENS, AIN'T THEY?

IT WAS TWO HOURS LATER THAT THE CHIEF'S SON RODE INTO CAMP, FLUSHED AND HAPPY FROM A LONG GALLOP THROUGH THE VALLEYS INTERLACING THE NEARBY HILLS...

HAIL, FLEET MUSTANG! MEET OUR FRIEND, THE BEAR SLAYER!

THE MIGHTY ONE HIMSELF! LONG HAVE I WAITED FOR THIS MOMENT!

A MERRY GRIN CREASING HIS BRONZED FACE, FLEET MUSTANG TOOK THE TRAPPER'S HAND IN A FIRM, CONFIDENT GRASP...

I HAVE PLANNED MANY THINGS TO CELEBRATE OUR FIRST MEETING, MY BROTHER! THERE SHALL BE MUCH SPORT, AND MANY FEATS OF STRENGTH BETWEEN US!

THAT'S A FIRST-RATE IDEA. WE'LL SEE IF YOU'RE AS TOUGH AND STRONG AS YOUR FATHER SAYS YOU ARE.

HIS WHOLE BODY ALIVE WITH LAUGHTER AND EXCITEMENT, THE YOUNG BRAVE FLUNG HIMSELF BACK ONTO HIS PONY...

COME THEN! THERE SHALL BE NO DELAY! FIRST THERE WILL BE THE MOST DIFFICULT FEAT OF ALL — THE FEAT AT WHICH I HAVE NEVER SO FAR SUCCEEDED!

IF IT'S WHAT I THINK IT IS, BOY, I'M NOT SURPRISED. IT SURE TAKES SOME PRACTICE.

SWINGING HIMSELF INTO THE SADDLE OF HIS HORSE, DAVY FOLLOWED FLEET MUSTANG, WHILE THE WHOOPING INDIAN VILLAGERS, ELATED AT THE THOUGHT OF A CONTEST, SET UP THE NECESSARIES FOR THE FIRST GAME.

YOU MUST RIDE HARD, BEAR SLAYER, AND WHILST IN FULL GALLOP, LEAN FROM THE SADDLE TO PLUCK UP THE SPEAR AND FLING IT INTO THE CENTRE OF THE TARGET.

DON'T WORRY, SON — I KNOW THE RULES. SHALL I GO FIRST?

THE BOY NODDED, AND DAVY TENSED HIS MIGHTY MUSCLES AS HE URGED HIS HORSE INTO A FLAT-OUT GALLOP!

WITH SPLIT-SECOND TIMING—FOR EVEN THE SLIGHTEST ERROR COULD HAVE MEANT A DANGEROUS FALL — THE TRAPPER HOOKED HIS BRAWNY FINGERS ROUND THE WOODEN SHAFT AND FLUNG FORWARD AND UP!

NEXT ON THE LIST WAS A SHOOTING CONTEST — FLEET MUSTANG'S BOW AGAINST LONG BETSEY. THIS TIME IT WAS THE INDIAN WHO BEGAN THE CONTEST..

GO TO THE BUSHES, BEAR SLAYER, AND HURL THAT PACKAGE AS FAR INTO THE AIR AS YOU CAN. THIS TIME I SHALL NOT FAIL.

AS THE BOY HAD ASKED, DAVY WALKED TO THE BUSHES AND TOSSED THE TARGET HIGH IN THE AIR...THEN TO THE WHOLE CAMP'S ASTONISHMENT, FLEET MUSTANG DROPPED HIS AIM AND LET FLY — *STRAIGHT AT THE TRAPPER!*

AAAGH! WHAT HAVE YOU DONE?

AIEEE! HE SEEKS TO KILL THE MIGHTY ONE!

PARALYSED WITH DISBELIEF, DAVY FELT A SHARP, SEARING PAIN IN HIS SHOULDER AS THE HURTLING SHAFT SPED PAST HIS EAR — *BUT IT WAS NOT CAUSED BY FLEET MUSTANG'S ARROW!*

AAAGH! WHAT IN HECK..?

...AND IN THE SAME INSTANT, DAVY HEARD A GRUNT OF AGONY IN THE BUSHES BEHIND HIM!

IT WAS A SOUND HEARD ALSO BY THE HUSHED SHASTAS, AND AS A MAN THEY RAN FORWARD TO THE TRAPPER'S SIDE...

YOU ARE HURT...

DON'T WORRY — IT'S ONLY A SCRATCH. THERE WAS SOME VARMINT LURKING BEHIND ME ALL SET TO LIFT MY HAIR.

I SAW HIS FACE IN THE INSTANT BEFORE I FIRED. FORGIVE ME IF I ALARMED YOU...

THE THREE MEN PUSHED THEIR WAY THROUGH THE BUSHES, ONLY TO FIND THAT THE MYSTERIOUS KILLER HAD VANISHED. HOWEVER, THE DROPPED TOMAHAWK GAVE THEM A LEAD...

AN OSAGE! SOME BUCK ON THE WATCH FOR SHASTA HORSES TO STEAL. NO DOUBT HE WAS TEMPTED BY SO GREAT A SCALP SET BEFORE HIM!

TOO BAD FOR HIM THAT FLEET MUSTANG WAS SUCH A FINE SHOT. BY THE BLOOD TRAIL, I CAN SEE HE'S NURSING A PRETTY SORE WOUND!

FURTHER SEARCHING BROUGHT FRESH HORSE TRACKS TO LIGHT, AND THE PARTY RETURNED EMPTY-HANDED TO THE CAMP...

YOU MUST REST YOUR WOUND, BEAR SLAYER. OUR CONTESTS ARE OVER FOR TODAY.

OKAY, FLEET MUSTANG. BUT TOMORROW I'M ALL SET TO START OUT FOR SOME HUNTING. I'LL BE AWAY ABOUT TWO MONTHS I GUESS.

DISAPPOINTMENT CLOUDED THE FEATURES OF THE FRIENDLY BOY, BUT HIS EYES LIT UP AS HIS FATHER DREW DAVY TO A HALT...

IT IS GOOD THAT YOU GO TRAPPING, FOR I HAVE A FAVOUR TO ASK OF YOU—A FAVOUR CONCERNING FLEET MUSTANG...

GO AHEAD MANY CLAWS. IF IT'S POSSIBLE, YOU CAN BET I'LL DO IT.

WILL YOU TAKE MY SON WITH YOU? THE BOY WILL LEARN MUCH IN THE COMPANY OF SO GREAT A HUNTER, AND BESIDES, I WOULD SEEK TO HAVE HIM UNDERSTAND MORE FULLY WAYS OF THE WHITE MAN.

I'D BE ONLY TOO GLAD, MANY CLAWS. FLEET MUSTANG'S A FINE BOY.

AIEE! THE SPIRITS SMILE ON ME THIS DAY!

IT WAS EARLY NEXT MORNING THAT THE TRAPPER AND HIS YOUNG COMPANION PREPARED TO LEAVE THE SHASTA CAMP. DAVY, ALTHOUGH HE HAD SLEPT WELL, FELT SLUGGISH AND DROWSY . . .

WHAT AILS MY BROTHER? ARE YOU SICK?

IT'S—IT'S NOTHING . . .

DAVY FORCED A GRIN AND TOOK FAREWELL OF THE OLD CHIEF. THEN HE AND FLEET MUSTANG TOOK THE TRAIL — A TRAIL WHICH, THE YOUNG BOY WAS SURE, WOULD LEAD TO FABULOUS ADVENTURE!

THE TWO COMRADES HAD SCARCELY GONE SIX MILES BEFORE DAVY BEGAN TO FEEL MORE AND MORE UNWELL. RED MISTS OF DIZZINESS SWEPT OVER HIM, AND HE REELED IN THE SADDLE . . .

MY BROTHER— YOU ARE LIKE A GHOST! YOU MUST STOP AND REST.

IT-IT'LL PASS—

BUT IN HIS HEART, DAVY KNEW THAT SOMETHING WAS VERY WRONG, AND WHEN FLEET MUSTANG DREW HIM OFF THE TRAIL TO AN ISOLATED WATERHOLE, THE TRAPPER MADE NO OFFER OF RESISTANCE. HALF-AN-HOUR LATER, DAVY WAS FLAT ON HIS BACK IN THE WELCOME SHADE OF A CLUMP OF WILLOW. HIS HEAD FELT STRANGELY LIGHT...

YOU ARE INDEED SICK! TELL ME WHAT I MUST DO!

WHITE SETTLEMENT — CANNON'S CROSSING. IT'S TEN MILES SOUTH EAST — GO THERE — FETCH A DOCTOR —

THE BOY NODDED. THEN, A FLASH OF INSPIRATION STRUCK HIM, AND HE GENTLY LIFTED THE TRAPPER AND DREW ASIDE HIS SHIRT. THE SIGHT WHICH MET HIS EYES MADE HIM DRAW A BREATH OF HORROR AND ANGUISH..

BEAR SLAYER! THE AXE WOUND YOU RECEIVED YESTERDAY — IT IS BAD MEDICINE — IT IS MANY COLOURS, AND SWOLLEN!

I — SHOULD HAVE REMEMBERED — THE OSAGES ARE — KEEN ON USING POISONED — WEAPONS —

WITHOUT ANOTHER MOMENT'S DELAY, FLEET MUSTANG SPRANG ONTO HIS PONY'S BACK...

I WILL TAKE YOUR HORSE WITH ME, LEST IT SHOULD ATTRACT THE ATTENTION OF ANYONE WHO WOULD SEEK TO HARM YOU. FEAR NOT I SHALL RETURN QUICKLY!

SO LONG, BOY— AND GOOD LUCK.

HIS HEAD SWIMMING, DAVY LAY SILENT, FIGHTING AGAINST THE AGONY OF HIS TORTURED SHOULDER. THEN, SUDDENLY, HE WAS AWARE OF A PARTY OF HORSEMEN, HALTED AT THE WATERHOLE...

OSAGE BUCKS—AND PAINTED FOR WAR! DURN IT, THEIR CHIEF'S GOT HIS ARM IN A SLING.

DAVY GATHERED FROM THEIR CONVERSATION THAT THE CHIEF'S NAME WAS LONG LANCE. AS HE LAY SILENT AMONGST THE CONCEALING GRASS, HE HEARD A LOT MORE . . .

A THOUSAND CURSES ON THIS WOUND! SOON I SHALL SEEK VENGEANCE ON THE SHASTA BUCK WHO DEALT ME THIS INJURY AND ROBBED ME OF THE BEAR SLAYER'S SCALP...

LONG LANCE WAS NONE OTHER THAN THE MYSTERIOUS ATTACKER WHO HAD STRUCK DAVY WITH THE POISONED AXE!

BUT MY CONSOLATION IS TO KNOW THAT THE BEAR SLAYER WILL BE DEAD BEFORE LONG! THE WOUND I GAVE HIM IS FULL OF THE DEADLY DRUG TO WHICH ONLY I HAVE THE ANTIDOTE!

THE SNEERING CHIEF TAPPED THE BEADED MEDICINE POUCH HANGING AT HIS WAIST, AND LAUGHED, MIRTHLESSLY. THEN HIS BROW DARKENED, AND HE BECAME MORE SERIOUS ..

NOW, MY BROTHERS, WE SHALL FOLLOW OUR VICTORY OVER THE WHITE HOMESTEAD WHICH WE ATTACKED YESTERDAY. WE SHALL RIDE TO THE SETTLEMENT CALLED CANNON'S CROSSING, AND WE SHALL SWEEP THROUGH LIKE A PRAIRIE FIRE, TAKING MANY SCALPS. SURPRISE WILL BE ON OUR SIDE, AND UNHARMED, WE WILL RETURN HOME BY WAY OF THE SHASTA CAMP, WHERE I SHALL EXACT REVENGE FOR THIS WOUND I BEAR

A COLD SWEAT BROKE OUT ON DAVY'S BROW AS THE OSAGES RODE AWAY. BOTH CANNON'S CROSSING AND THE SHASTA CAMP WERE IN DEADLY DANGER — AND HE COULD DO NOTHING! HE TRIED TO RISE, BUT THE EFFORT COST HIM DEAR — HE FELL BACK, UNCONSCIOUS!

MEANWHILE, FLEET MUSTANG, SWEAT-SOAKED AND TRAVEL-STAINED, HAD REACHED CANNON'S CROSSING. URGENTLY, HE GALLOPED INTO THE MAIN STREET...

LOOK — AN INJUN!

HE'S GOT SOME NERVE, COMIN' HERE!

NERVE? THAT'S PUTTIN' IT MILDLY, AIN'T IT? I'LL SHOW THE VARMINT WHAT WE THINK OF DIRTY RED HEATHENS.

EVEN IF THE TOWNSFOLK HAD KNOWN THE DIFFERENCE BETWEEN A SHASTA AND AN OSAGE, FEW OF THEM WOULD HAVE CARED. BELLOWING AND ROARING THEIR HATE, THEY DRAGGED THE WINDED, SEMI-CONSCIOUS BRAVE DOWN THE MAIN STREET...

LYNCH HIM!

THIS'LL LARN THE VARMINT TO COME BRASSIN' HIS WAY AROUND WHITE FOLKS!

AS THE RAGE-MADDENED SETTLERS SAT HIM ON A HORSE BENEATH THE DREADED HANGING TREE, FLEET MUSTANG TRIED IN VAIN TO TELL THEM OF DAVY'S PLIGHT..

STOP! WAIT! YOU KNOW NOT WHAT YOU DO! I BRING NEWS OF DAVY CROCKETT — HE IS DYING —

SHUT YOUR MOUTH, YOU RED SCUM! THE ONLY THING YOU KNOW ABOUT CROCKETT IS WHERE HIS SCALP'S PLACED.

AN EXPECTANT HUSH FELL OVER THE CROWD AS RUBE SHULTON HIMSELF PREPARED TO PLACE THE HEMP NOOSE AROUND FLEET MUSTANG'S NECK.

I KNOW NOT WHAT MAKES YOU DO THIS TO ME, WHITE MAN, BUT REALISE THAT YOU KILL THE BEAR SLAYER AS WELL AS ME!

SAVE YOUR BREATH..YOU RED CUR. I WANT TO HEAR YOU SCREAM FOR MERCY!

THEN, SUDDENLY, THE AIR WAS TORN ASUNDER BY A CHORUS OF SAVAGE YELLS! LONG LANCE'S OSAGES HAD HIT TOWN!

INJUN ATTACK!

GRAB YOUR GUNS!

GRIMLY, FLEET MUSTANG WATCHED AS THE SCREECHING OSAGES CAME THUNDERING DOWN THE MAIN STREET.

THOUGH LONG LANCE HAD BEEN CONFIDENT OF SCORING AN EASY COUP, HE FOUND THAT HE HAD HIS HANDS FULL WITH THE DETERMINED SETTLERS ...

KEEP AT IT, BOYS! WE'LL GET 'EM RUNNIN' YET!

THEN, SAVAGELY, LONG LANCE ORDERED HIS BRAVES TO LIGHT FIRE ARROWS!

BURN! BURN AND KILL!

HORRIFIED, FLEET MUSTANG WATCHED THE PITCHED BATTLE ENACTED BEFORE HIS EYES ... FOR A MOMENT, HE THOUGHT OF URGING THE HORSE BENEATH HIM TO CARRY HIM TO SAFETY— BUT THEN HIS HOPES WERE DASHED TO THE GROUND!

IT CANNOT BE —BUT, YES! IT IS THE SHASTA CUR WHO CHEATED ME OF THE BEAR SLAYER'S SCALP! ONHEY, MANITOU IS INDEED GOOD TO ME!

WHOOPING WITH SAVAGE GLEE, LONG LANCE SPURRED FORWARD AND FLUNG HIS WAR CLUB AT FLEET MUSTANG'S DEFENCELESS HEAD!

HAGA! KEEP HIM SAFE, SNAKE FANG, WE WILL HAVE MUCH SPORT WITH HIM BEFORE HE DIES!

THE SETTLERS WERE UNDER THE IMPRESSION THAT LONG LANCE'S OSAGES HAD ESCAPED UNSCATHED — BUT THEY WERE WRONG! EXPERT HORSEMEN THAT THEY WERE, THE BRAVES HAD ALL KEPT THEIR SADDLES — BUT MANY OF THEM WERE WOUNDED, SOME OF THEM BADLY . . .

MANITOU HAS GIVEN US MANY COUPS, BUT HE HAS ALSO GIVEN US MANY WOUNDS TO LICK. THERE IS A WATERHOLE FURTHER ON. THERE WE SHALL REST AND MAKE CAMP FOR THE NIGHT. THERE I SHALL BARE MY OWN WOUND, FOR ALREADY IT FEELS BETTER.

THE WATERHOLE TO WHICH LONG LANCE LED HIS MEN WAS THE ONLY ONE FOR MILES AROUND IN THAT RUGGED COUNTRY, THE ONE WHERE FLEET MUSTANG HAD LEFT DAVY CROCKETT!

THE HARD GROUND WILL BE OUR BEDS TONIGHT, MY BROTHERS. REST WELL, AND WE WILL RIDE ON TO OUR CAMP IN THE MORNING.

LONG LANCE'S WORDS CAME FAINTLY TO THE EXHAUSTED TRAPPER, BUT IN THEM LAY THAT FAINT RAY OF HOPE WHICH MADE DAVY SUMMON UP ALL HIS FINAL RESOURCES OF STRENGTH IN A DO-OR-DIE EFFORT... THAT NIGHT, WHEN THE CAMPFIRES HAD BURNED LOW, AND THE SINGLE SENTRY LEANED SLEEPILY ON HIS SPEAR...

MY – ONLY CHANCE – MUST GET THAT ANTIDOTE – IN HIS POUCH –

INCH BY INCH, THE TRAPPER WORKED HIS WAY THROUGH THE TALL GRASS, CLOSER AND CLOSER TO LONG LANCE'S SLEEPING FIGURE! ONE SLIP WOULD HAVE MEANT DEATH...

IF HE WAKES UP...

DAVY SLID HIS FINGERS INTO THE MEDICINE BAG AND CRUNCHED THE BERRIES HE FOUND THERE. HE HAD HOPED THAT THE ANTIDOTE WOULD WORK QUICKLY ENOUGH FOR HIM TO RESCUE FLEET MUSTANG, BUT AS HE CRAWLED BACK TO HIS HIDING PLACE, THE EFFORT TOOK ITS TOLL... ONCE AGAIN, HE SLIPPED INTO THE BLACK VOID OF SENSELESSNESS!

WHEN DAVY CAME ROUND, THE SUN HUNG LIKE AN ORANGE FIRE-BALL IN A FAULTLESS SKY OF BRILLIANT BLUE. GINGERLY, HE EASED HIMSELF TO HIS FEET — AND A SUDDEN FLOW OF RELIEF SWEPT OVER HIM AS HE DISCOVERED THAT HIS FEVER HAD PASSED! THEN HIS MEMORY CAME FLOODING IN, AND HE REALISED THAT LONG LANCE AND HIS PARTY HAD GONE . . .

BY GLORY! I'LL HAVE TO ACT FAST! IF I START WALKING NOW, I'LL REACH THE SHASTA CAMP IN ABOUT AN HOUR AND A HALF.

WHEN THE TRAPPER REACHED THE REDSKIN VILLAGE, HIS NEWS SET THE TRIBE AFIRE.

QUICKLY, MY BROTHERS! TO ARMS! MY SON MUST BE SAVED BEFORE THE TREACHEROUS OSAGES TORTURE HIM AT THEIR STAKES!

LEND ME A HORSE, MANY CLAWS — I'M COMING WITH YOU!

SLOWLY, THE CHIEF SPELLED OUT THE GRIM MESSAGE, WHILE SULLEN MUTTERINGS BROKE OUT ALL ALONG THE INDIAN COLUMN...

THEY SAY THAT OUR CAMP IS UNDER ATTACK FROM WHITE MEN! THEY ARE MANY — AND THIRSTY FOR BLOOD!

THE BLASTING TRUTH HIT DAVY CROCKETT LIKE A BACKHANDED SLAP IN THE FACE!

IT'S THE SETTLERS FROM CANNON'S CROSSING! LONG LANCE'S OSAGES SACKED THEIR TOWN, AND THE WHITE FOLK ARE TOO HET UP TO CARE WHERE THEY GET THEIR REVENGE! THIS IS SERIOUS, MANY CLAWS — DEADLY SERIOUS!

WHAT MUST I DO? MANITOU GUIDE ME! MUST I ABANDON FLEET MUSTANG AND SAVE MY VILLAGE — OR MUST I RISK THE LIVES OF SQUAWS, OLD MEN AND PAPOOSES TO RESCUE MY SON?

HIS FACE TWISTED BY THE AGONY OF THAT AWFUL DILEMMA, MANY CLAWS DUMBLY SEARCHED THE GRAVEN FACES OF HIS BRAVES FOR SOME ANSWER. FOR LONG MOMENTS THERE WAS A SILENCE SO HEAVY THAT IT SEEMED TO PRESS DOWN ON EVERY MAN PRESENT ~ BUT AT LAST A CALM, REASONING VOICE BROKE THE SPELL!

THERE IS ONLY ONE THING FOR YOU TO DO, MANY CLAWS! YOU MUST RIDE ON AND ATTACK THE OSAGE VILLAGE. DO NOT DIVIDE YOUR FORCES, OR YOU WILL NOT BE STRONG ENOUGH FOR SPEEDY VICTORY...

BUT, BEAR SLAYER ~ WHAT OF MY VILLAGE?

SHOULD YOU SEND BRAVES BACK TO DEFEND YOUR VILLAGE, MUCH BLOOD WILL BE SENSELESSLY SPILLED. NO! IT IS FOR ME TO RIDE BACK TO THE CAMP AND PERSUADE MY WHITE BROTHERS TO CEASE THEIR FOLLY.

A LOW RUMBLE OF APPROVAL ROLLED ALONG THE MIGHTY COLUMN, AND MANY CLAWS CLASPED THE HAND OF HIS FRIEND IN A STRONG, THANKFUL GRASP...

WHAT YOU SAY IS TRUE, MY BROTHER. MAY MANITOU SMILE UPON YOU!

AND YOU, MANY CLAWS. DON'T WORRY ~ EVERYTHING'S GOING TO BE ALL RIGHT!

LONG, RAKING STRIDES EATING UP THE MILES BACK TO THE SHASTA CAMP, DAVY'S LEAN INDIAN MUSTANG FLEW UP THE FINAL SLOPE AND TORE ACROSS THE CREST OF THE RISE FROM WHICH THE TRAPPER COULD SEE THE WHOLE GRIM SCENE SPREAD OUT BELOW...

BY HOKEY! THEY'RE HEADIN' IN FOR THE ATTACK!

LIKE A THUNDERBOLT, DAVY RACED DOWN THE HILL AT A RECKLESS GALLOP, TURF AND GRASS FLYING FROM THE CHOPPING HOOFS OF HIS LATHERED HORSE. RIDING INTO THE VERY TEETH OF THE ATTACK, RISKING DEATH AT EVERY MOMENT FROM A SCORE OF BULLETS, HE DREW HIS MUSTANG TO A SLITHERING HALT!

IT'S DAVY CROCKETT!

WHAT'S HE DOIN?

IF HE AIMS TO PUT US OFF, HE'S GOT ANOTHER THINK COMIN'.

A BABBLE OF QUESTIONS HIT THE STALWART TRAPPER'S EARS, BUT HIS CURT VOICE SNAPPED THE IMPATIENT SETTLERS INTO INSTANT SILENCE!

SHUT UP AND LISTEN! YOU CRAZY FOOLS ARE AS CLOSE TO BEIN' DOWNRIGHT MURDERERS AS YOU'LL EVER BE! DON'T YOU KNOW THERE'S NOBODY BUT WOMEN, AN' KIDS, AN' OLD MEN IN THAT VILLAGE?

DAVY NOTICED THE NUMBER OF SETTLERS WHO STARTED VISIBLY AT HIS FIERY WORDS, AND FOR LONG MOMENTS THERE WAS SILENCE. THEN, RUBE SHULTON SPOKE...

WHAT DID *THEIR* MEN CARE ABOUT OUR WOMEN AN' KIDS?

WHEN DAVY SPOKE, HIS VOICE SNAPPED THROUGH THE AIR LIKE A WHIPLASH...

IN THE FIRST PLACE, THE INJUNS WHO CLEANED YOUR PLACE UP WERE OSAGES, NOT SHASTAS. IN THE SECOND PLACE, THE SHASTAS ARE AWAY LICKIN' BLAZES OUT OF THE OSAGE. I KNOW WHAT I'M TALKIN' ABOUT, SHULTON.

DURN IT, SHULTON, HE WOULDN'T HAVE RISKED HIS NECK TO STOP US FOR NOTHIN'. I RECKON THERE'S TRUTH IN WHAT HE SAYS.

DAVY SMILED SLOWLY, AND TURNED FOR A MOMENT TO LOOK ACROSS TO THE SHASTA CAMP, WHERE WOMEN AND CHILDREN LOOKED AT HIM WITH SILENT THANKS AND ADMIRATION. THEN HE SPOKE ONCE AGAIN TO THE SETTLERS . . .

I CAN APPRECIATE YOU FOLKS GETTING HET UP — HOSTILE BUCKS DESERVE TO BE TAUGHT A LESSON. SO HOW ABOUT COMIN' WITH ME TO ADD OUR STRENGTH TO THE SHASTAS AND GIVE THE OSAGES A LICKING THEY'LL NEVER FORGET?

THAT'S SENSE, DAVY — WE'RE WITH YOU!

LEAD ON, DAVY — WE'VE GOT A BIG DEBT TO PAY!

MEANWHILE, IN THE OSAGE CAMP, BRAVES WERE RUSHING HITHER AND THITHER IN A FRANTIC EFFORT TO ARM THEMSELVES. A LOOKOUT HAD SPOTTED MANY CLAWS' SHASTAS HEADING INTO THE ATTACK!

QUICKLY, MY BROTHERS! OUR ENEMIES ARE UPON US!

HA! NOW FEEL THE MIGHT OF THE SHASTAS, YOU DOG!

YELLING THEIR SAVAGE WAR-CRIES, THEY PASSED RIGHT THROUGH THE VILLAGE, LEAVING BEHIND THEM A TRAIL OF DESTRUCTION!

MANY CLAWS MADE AS IF TO START FORWARD, BUT LONG LANCE BROUGHT THE KNIFE CLOSER.

STAY, MANY CLAWS! IF YOU OR ANY OF YOUR SHASTA CURS MAKES A MOVE, YOUR SON DIES!

MANY CLAWS HAD NO CHOICE BUT TO OBEY. A WRONG MOVE COULD MEAN THE END OF HIS SON... BUT THEN SOMETHING HAPPENED WHICH BROUGHT THE SHASTA CHIEF'S HEART INTO HIS MOUTH...

NO! IT CANNOT BE!

DAVY CROCKETT AND HIS SETTLER REINFORCEMENTS HAD SWEPT INTO VIEW!

WE'D BETTER MAKE A SHOW OF RETIRING — RIDE OUT OF SIGHT OVER THE CREST. WE'D BETTER KEEP GOING, TOO, FOR THE OSAGES ARE BOUND TO FOLLOW UP AN' SEE WHAT WE'RE UP TO. BUT THE MINUTE WE'RE OUT OF SIGHT FOR THOSE FEW MOMENTS, I'LL CUT OFF TO THE SIDE ...

WHERE A REGIMENT COULD FAIL, ONE MAN COULD WIN, AND WHILE THE OSAGES ARE BUSY GLOATING OVER YOUR RETREAT, I'LL TRY A DASH THROUGH THE CAMP TO GRAB FLEET MUSTANG.

IT IS OUR ONLY CHANCE, MY BROTHER, AND YOU ARE INDEED A TRUE FRIEND TO TAKE SUCH A RISK.

THE COMBINED FORCES OF THE SHASTA AND THE SETTLERS FROM CANNON'S CROSSING RODE OVER THE CREST OF THE SLOPE, FOLLOWED BY DERISIVE YELLS OF TRIUMPH FROM THE OSAGE SURVIVORS ... BUT ONCE OUT OF VIEW ...

IT SHOULD BE MY TASK TO RISK MY LIFE IN THIS MANNER, BEAR SLAYER.

THE OSAGES WOULD NOTICE YOUR ABSENCE A SIGHT QUICKER THAN THEY'D NOTICE MINE, MY BROTHER. SO LONG!

THEN, JUST WHEN IT SEEMED THAT THEY HAD NO MORE STRENGTH LEFT TO FIGHT, A SOUND CAME TO THE EARS OF DAVY AND FLEET MUSTANG WHICH SENT NEW BLOOD COURSING THROUGH THEIR VEINS!

ONHEY! FLEE LIKE THE CURS YOU ARE!

THE SETTLERS AND THE SHASTAS HAD RETURNED!

THE OSAGES SPLIT UP AND RAN AS THE VENGEFUL HORDE CUT THROUGH THEM. THEIR TERRIFIED YELLS MINGLED WITH THE CLUBBING THUMP OF GUN-BUTTS, THE DEADLY SINGING OF PLUCKED BOWSTRINGS . . .

SPRINGING INTO ACTION, DAVY KNEED HIS HORSE FORWARD AND SET OFF IN IMMEDIATE PURSUIT...

LEAVE HIM TO ME! I'VE GOT A FEVER AND A DURNED SORE SHOULDER TO PAY HIM FOR!

DAVY'S FLEET MUSTANG RAPIDLY OVERTOOK THE SNARLING CHIEF...

I KNOW NOT HOW YOU ESCAPED MY POISON, DOG, BUT NOW YOU SHALL SURELY DIE!

NOT BY YOUR HAND, LONG LANCE!

HIS FEATURES CONTORTED INTO A VICIOUS LEER OF HATE LONG LANCE HURLED HIS RAZOR-TIPPED SPEAR FULL AT THE TRAPPER'S CHEST — BUT IN THAT SAME INSTANT, DAVY SPRANG!

GOOD THROW, LONG LANCE — BUT NOT GOOD ENOUGH!

WITH BATED BREATH, THE SHASTAS HAD MOVED FORWARD, BETTER TO WATCH THE LIFE-OR-DEATH STRUGGLE. THEN, AS HE SAW DAVY AT LONG LANCE'S MERCY, FLEET MUSTANG FLUNG HIS HORSE INTO A BREAKNECK GALLOP!

THE TREACHEROUS COWARD! HE WILL STRIKE THE HELPLESS BEAR SLAYER DOWN!

THE BOY COULD NEVER HAVE HOPED TO REACH LONG LANCE BEFORE HE STRUCK THE DEATH BLOW — *BUT HALFWAY BETWEEN THEM LAY THE OSAGE CHIEF'S DISCARDED SPEAR!*

THIS TIME, I *MUST* SUCCEED!

AS THE REST OF THE SHASTAS AND THE SETTLERS GALLOPED ACROSS, DAVY TOOK FLEET MUSTANG'S HAND IN A WARM, FRIENDLY GRASP...

BOY, YOU'RE MORE THAN JUST A BRAVE — YOU'RE A HERO OF YOUR TRIBE, AND FIT TO BE THE SON OF A GREAT CHIEF!

AIEEE! AND I HAVE AT LAST PASSED THE TEST WHICH SO MANY TIMES I HAD FAILED!

IT WAS NOT OFTEN, EVEN IN TIMES OF BLISSFUL PEACE, THAT RED MAN AND WHITE SAT DOWN TOGETHER TO FEAST AND MAKE MERRY, BUT THAT NIGHT, IN THE SHASTA CAMP, THERE WAS A CELEBRATION THAT LASTED LONG INTO THE NEXT DAY...

...IT WAS A FEAST IN HONOUR OF FLEET MUSTANG, AND IN HONOUR OF THE KING OF THE STALWART FRONTIERSMEN WHO HAD RISKED ALL TO THROW UPON THE BOY THE MANTLE OF TRUE MANHOOD!

KIT CARSON—
INDIAN TAMER

YELLOW SHIRT WAS DEAD! THE GREAT WAR CHIEF, WHO HAD MADE THE TONTO APACHES FEARED THROUGHOUT ARIZONA, HAD AT LAST DEPARTED...
THE COUNCIL OF CHIEFTAINS VIEWED HIS PASSING WITH MIXED FEELINGS. THEY HAD REGARDED YELLOW SHIRT AS A GOD, AND ONLY HIS IRON CHARACTER HAD KEPT THEM ON THE WAR-TRAIL.
FOR YEARS MANY HAD HOPED THAT HE WOULD MAKE PEACE WITH THE WHITES, BUT THERE HAD ALWAYS BEEN SOMETHING NEW TO KEEP HIM FROM DOING SO. NOW AT LAST THEY HAD A CHANCE...

WHAT SHALL WE DO, BROTHERS, MAKE PEACE, OR CONTINUE TO WAR ON THE WHITE-EYES?

MY FATHER CAUSED THIS TRIBE TO BE FEARED THE LENGTH AND BREADTH OF OUR TERRITORY. HE MADE US STRONG— WOULD YOU RUIN ALL HE HAS DONE?

THE TONGUES OF THE YOUNG SPEAK BEFORE THEIR THOUGHTS ARE FORMED! AT ONE TIME IT WAS NECESSARY TO MAKE WAR—BUT THAT TIME IS GONE NOW, FOR THE WHITE-EYES ALSO WANT PEACE!

SEVERAL DAYS LATER, AFTER NEGOTIATIONS WITH THE ARMY HAD BEEN MADE, THE TONTO CHIEFS SET OFF FOR FORT GRENNELL TO SIGN A TREATY... BUT THE MIND OF BURNING LANCE REMAINED UNCHANGED...

THEY CAN CRAWL TO THE PONY SOLDIERS— BUT I SHALL NEVER DO SO!

AT FORT GRENNELL, COLONEL NELSON, THE COMMANDING OFFICER OF THE GARRISON, WELCOMED A NEW ARRIVAL...

GLAD YOU COULD MAKE IT, KIT. WE NEEDED A GOOD INTERPRETER FOR THESE PEACE TALKS AND I THOUGHT YOU'D BE THE BEST MAN FOR THE JOB!

GLAD TO HELP, COLONEL. I HEAR I ONLY JUST MADE IT IN TIME!

IN HIS OFFICE, THE CAPTAIN EXPLAINED THAT THERE WERE STILL TROUBLES TO BE FACED ONCE THE TREATY WAS SIGNED.
A HUGE OUTLAW GANG— RENEGADE AMERICANS, MEXICANS AND INDIANS— WAS CAMPED ON THE OTHER SIDE OF THE MEXICAN BORDER.
"LOS RENEGADOS" MADE THEIR CROOKED LIVING BY SELLING GUNS AND AMMUNITION TO THE TONTOS. THE U.S. ARMY COULD DO NOTHING TO STOP THEM, FOR THEY HAD NO JURISDICTION IN MEXICO.
THE COLONEL FELT THAT "LOS RENEGADOS" WOULD DO EVERYTHING THEY COULD TO MAKE THE APACHES RETURN TO THE WAR-PATH.
THAT WAS ANOTHER REASON WHY HE HAD SENT FOR KIT'S HELP...

...SO YOU SEE, KIT, OUR PROBLEMS WON'T BE AT AN END EVEN WHEN THE TREATY'S MADE. SOMEHOW, SOMEONE HAS GOT TO MAKE THOSE NO-GOOD RENEGADES COME ACROSS THE BORDER SO THAT THE CAVALRY CAN DEAL WITH 'EM!

WELL, COLONEL, JUST AS SOON AS THESE PEACE-TALKS ARE CLEARED UP, I'LL SEE WHAT I CAN DO

AN HOUR LATER, THE TONTO CHIEFS ARRIVED AT THE FORT AND, WITH KIT INTERPRETING, NEGOTIATIONS BEGAN...

BUT HIGH ON A BLUFF OVERLOOKING THE FORT, A LONE APACHE HORSEMAN SURVEYED THE SCENE, A LOOK OF CONTEMPT ON HIS YOUNG FACE. IT WAS BURNING LANCE, COME TO WITNESS WHAT HE CONSIDERED THE DOWNFALL OF HIS TRIBE...

SO! THE TREATY IS MADE. IF MY PEOPLE REFUSE TO REMEMBER MY FATHER, THEN I ALONE SHALL KEEP HIS MEMORY ALIVE! THE WHITE-EYES WILL HAVE GOOD CAUSE TO REMEMBER BURNING LANCE, SON OF YELLOW SHIRT!

...WHILE DOWN IN THE FORT, THE TALKS WERE BEING WOUND UP, BOTH PARTIES HIGHLY SATISFIED—

WELL, THAT SEEMS TO BE EVERYTHING, COLONEL. THE CHIEF WANTS YOU TO KNOW THAT HE AND HIS PEOPLE INTEND TO LIVE IN PEACE FROM NOW ON. THE TONTOS GIVE THEIR WORD THAT THEY SHALL NEVER GO TO WAR AGAIN!

THAT'S FINE, KIT. I WISH THE TONTOS A LONG PROSPERITY, CHIEF.

FURIOUS, BURNING LANCE WHEELED HIS PONY AROUND AND HEADED SOUTHWARDS TOWARDS THE BORDER. HE NEEDED HELP TO MAKE GOOD HIS BOAST AND THOUGHT HE KNEW WHERE TO GET IT...

IT WAS NOT LONG BEFORE BURNING LANCE REACHED HIS DESTINATION—THE NATURAL FORTRESS WHICH WAS THE CAMP OF LOS RENEGADOS. HERE THE RENEGADES HELD OUT AGAINST THE FEW SALLIES WHICH THE MEXICAN ARMY MADE FROM TIME TO TIME.

TELL YOUR LEADER, CARLOS BURGESS, THAT BURNING LANCE OF THE TONTOS WISHES TO SEE HIM!

SOON, BURNING LANCE WAS TALKING TO THE RASCALLY HALF-CASTE LEADER OF LOS RENEGADOS, CARLOS BURGESS...

I HAVE A PLAN WHICH WILL MAKE LOS RENEGADOS RICH AND THE APACHES OF YELLOW SHIRT FEARED AGAIN. I CAN LEAD YOU TO PALEFACE FARMS AND HOMESTEADS OVER THE BORDER— YOU AND YOUR MEN WILL HAVE MUCH LOOT. THE TONTOS WILL BE BLAMED FOR OUR RAIDS SO YOU HAVE NOTHING TO FEAR FROM THE SOLDIERS. MY PEOPLE WILL BE FORCED TO TAKE THE WAR-TRAIL AGAIN!

BURGESS GRINNED CRAFTILY. HE HAD BEEN RACKING HIS BRAINS TO THINK OF SOME WAY TO GET HIS ONE TIME CUSTOMERS' BACK ON THE WAR-PATH— AND NOW HE HAD IT!

THAT SOUNDS A FINE IDEA, BURNING LANCE. GIVE ME AND MY MEN TIME TO BREAK CAMP AND WE'LL MEET YOU TWO MILES OVER THE BORDER AT NOON TOMORROW.

VERY WELL. I SHALL STAY HERE TONIGHT AND IN THE MORNING WILL RETURN TO THE CAMP OF THE TONTOS TO GET MY WEAPONS!

THE MORNING AFTER THE TREATY HAD BEEN SIGNED, KIT LEFT THE FORT TO SEE IF HE COULD LOCATE LOS RENEGADOS' CAMP.

THE EAGLE-EYED SCOUT SOON DISCOVERED BURNING LANCE'S TRACKS LEADING TOWARDS THE BORDER. HERE AT LEAST WAS SOME CLUE. HE BEGAN TO FOLLOW THE TRAIL...

THUNDER, BOY, THESE HORSE PRINTS MAY WELL LEAD US TO THE OUTLAWS. IT'S A HUNCH BUT I'VE GOT A FEELING IT WILL BE WORTH IT...

NEAR THE BORDER, THE TRAIL PASSED A WATER-HOLE. KIT WAS GRATEFUL FOR THIS CHANCE TO QUENCH HIS THIRST. BUT AS HE BENT TO DRINK...

YOU SHALL BE THE FIRST TO DIE BY THE HAND OF YELLOW-SHIRT'S SON, WHITE-EYES!

BY JUPITER! AN APACHE!

A HOT FLUSH OF SHAME CREPT ACROSS THE YOUNG BRAVES FACE. HE DREW HIMSELF UP, READY TO DIE PROUDLY...

KILL ME NOW, PALEFACE, AND MAKE YOUR BULLET FLY TRUE THE SPIRIT OF YELLOW SHIRT, MY FATHER, SHALL NOT BE ASHAMED OF ME

YELLOW SHIRT WAS A GREAT FRIEND OF MINE — IT WOULDN'T DO FOR ME TO KILL HIS SON NOW, SUPPOSE YOU EXPLAIN WHY YOU ATTACKED ME

KIT TOLD BURNING LANCE THAT HE HAD KNOWN, YELLOW SHIRT FOR MANY YEARS BEFORE THE CHIEF DIED. WHEN THE SCOUT MENTIONED HIS NAME, THE SCOWL CLEARED FROM THE YOUNG APACHE'S FACE...

SO YOU ARE LONGHAIR! MY FATHER SPOKE OF YOU MANY TIMES — OFTEN HE LISTENED TO YOUR WORDS, FOR HE SAID THAT THEY WERE WISE. I AM GLAD, NOW, THAT I DID NOT KILL YOU

YOU'VE GOT TO REMEMBER, BURNING LANCE, THAT YOUR FATHER WAS A MAN OF HIS TIME. HE FOUGHT BECAUSE HE HAD TO. BUT THINGS HAVE CHANGED NOW— THE HOUR HAS COME WHEN THE APACHE NATION AND THE PALEFACE NATION SHOULD LIVE IN PEACE.

BUT THE APACHE WAS STILL NOT YET CONVINCED...

BUT MY FATHER WAS A GREAT WARRIOR. MUST I BECOME LIKE AN OLD WOMAN AND NOT FOLLOW IN HIS FOOTSTEPS? AM I TO END MY DAYS CUTTING CORN AND MAKING BLANKETS?

THERE IS NO NEED FOR EITHER EXTREME. YOU ARE STILL YOUNG AND HAVE MUCH TO LEARN. IF YOU WISH TO FIGHT, THEN JOIN THE CAVALRY— BECOME A SCOUT, AND FIGHT MEN LIKE LOS RENEGADOS WHO PREY ON RED MEN AND WHITE TOGETHER.

MY FATHER SPOKE WELL OF YOU, LONGHAIR. HE OFTEN TOOK YOUR ADVICE. I, WHO AM AS NOTHING COMPARED WITH YELLOW SHIRT SHOULD DO LIKEWISE IF IT IS NOT TOO LATE.

WHAT DO YOU MEAN, TOO LATE?

BURNING LANCE TOLD OF THE PLAN HE HAD MADE WITH CARLOS BURGESS...

EVEN NOW LOS RENEGADOS ARE PREPARING TO RIDE FOR THE BORDER, LONGHAIR!

THESE MEN ARE EVIL. THEY MUST BE BROUGHT TO JUSTICE. CAN YOU HELP ME CAPTURE THEM IF I GET THE CAVALRY'S HELP?

KIT TRIED HARD TO CONVINCE RUNNING WOLF, BUT THE OLD CHIEF WAS ADAMANT THE APACHES WERE NOT GOING TO WAR AGAIN! EVENTUALLY, FOR THERE WAS LITTLE TIME TO BE LOST, KIT RODE FOR THE FORT, LEAVING BURNING LANCE IN HIS VILLAGE.

WHILE KIT RODE TO WARN THE GARRISON, BURNING LANCE GALLOPED IN THE OTHER DIRECTION, INTENT ON TELLING LOS RENEGADOS THAT THE CAVALRY WOULD BE OUT TO MEET THEM

...WHILE BACK AT THE FORT —

COLONEL NELSON! NOW'S OUR CHANCE TO GET LOS RENEGADOS. THEY'LL BE OVER THE BORDER BY NOON! WE'LL HAVE TO MUSTER ALL THE MEN YOU CAN SPARE TO DEAL WITH THEM!

RIGHT YOU ARE, KIT, I'LL MAKE SURE THE MEN ARE READY TO LEAVE IN TEN MINUTES!

THE COLONEL WAS AS GOOD AS HIS WORD. TEN MINUTES LATER...

BUT MEANWHILE...

STOP! THE CAVALRY ARE RIDING TO CAPTURE YOU! YOU MUST RETURN.

ARE YOU CRAZY? WE'RE AFTER LOOT— WE CAN'T GO BACK NOW, MY MEN WOULD NEVER ALLOW IT!

THE APACHE EXPLAINED WHAT HAD HAPPENED. BUT THE GREEDY OUTLAW LEADER WANTED HIS EXCURSION OVER THE BORDER TO BE PROFITABLE. QUICKLY A NEW PLAN FORMED IN HIS CRAFTY BRAIN...

SAY—HOW ABOUT LEADING YOUR TONTOS INTO A TRAP? THE BIG MEXICAN RANCHERS NEED SLAVES, AND THEY AIN'T WORRIED ABOUT WHERE THEIR LABOUR COMES FROM! WHAT DO YOU SAY? THERE'LL BE A BIG CUT IN IT FOR YOU!

I WOULD NEVER AGREE TO SUCH TREACHERY!

BUT AN EVEN MATCH WAS NOT THE RENEGADES' IDEA OF FIGHTING. CAUGHT BETWEEN THE APACHES AND THE CAVALRY THEY HASTILY THREW DOWN THEIR GUNS AND RAISED THEIR ARMS.

DON'T SHOOT, CARSON! WE SURRENDER...

SO YOU AREN'T AS BRAVE WHEN THE ODDS ARE THE SAME. YOU'LL ALL GET A TRIAL AT FORT GRENNELL OKAY, MEN, HOGTIE THESE CRITTURS AND TAKE 'EM BACK TO THE JAIL

IT WAS WITH GREAT SATISFACTION THAT THE THREE MEN WATCHED THE TONTOS AND THE CAVALRYMEN BINDING THE RENEGADES...

AS YOU ONCE SAID, LONGHAIR, THESE ARE THE KIND OF MEN WHO SHOULD BE WARRED AGAINST. I WANTED TO FIGHT, BUT I DID NOT KNOW *WHO* TO FIGHT FROM NOW ON MY TRIBE AND I WILL MAKE WAR ON THE TREACHEROUS MEN WHO CAUSE BROTHERS TO KILL ONE ANOTHER!

GOOD FOR YOU, BURNING LANCE TOGETHER, WE'LL MAKE A GREAT TEAM I'VE GOT A FEELING THAT BETWEEN US WE'RE SOON GOING TO MAKE THIS COUNTRY FIT FOR BOTH OUR FOLKS TO LIVE IN!

Chapter 1. THE TRACKERS

TWO MEN DEDICATED TO THE CAUSE OF JUSTICE...BUCK JONES, SHERIFF OF ALKALI CITY...AND ROSS ARMSTRONG, PARTNERING BUCK ON A FINAL MISSION AFTER SIX MONTHS AS HIS DEPUTY...

FRESNO AND BROPHY SLOWED TO A WALK HERE. THAT'S CLEAR FROM THE SHORTENED STRIDE OF THEIR PONIES. I'D SAY WE CAN COUNT ON CATCHING UP WITH 'EM PRETTY SOON.

AIN'T NO REASON WHY WE SHOULDN'T, BUCK. THEY DON'T KNOW WE'RE TAILING 'EM.

THEY REACHED THE MESA'S SOUTH RIM AND LOOKED DOWN ON A LAND MASKED BY TREES AND CHAPARRAL. A BLUE-GREY COIL ROSE THINLY INTO THE SHIMMERING SKY...

IT LOOKS LIKE WE'VE CAUGHT UP WITH 'EM, BUCK. AND THEY'RE OFF-GUARD, ELSE THEY WOULDN'T HAVE LIT A FIRE.

JUST THE SAME, WE WON'T MOVE IN BALD-HEADED. WE'LL SPLIT UP AND WORK CLOSE FROM TWO DIRECTIONS!

BROPHY WAS NOT WORRIED. HE WAS NOT THE KIND TO SURRENDER HIS LIBERTY LIGHTLY, ANY MORE THAN FRESNO WAS. BUT AT PRESENT HE FONDLY IMAGINED HE WAS IN NO DANGER OF LOSING IT...

I GUESS MAYBE I'M TOO EDGY, AT THAT, BROPHY. ANYHOW, YOU KEEP THE FIRE GOING WHILE I GO BACK TO THAT WATER-HOLE!

FRESNO WENT OFF THROUGH THE CHAPARRAL...WHICH SPELT BAD LUCK FOR THE PLAN BUCK HAD IN MIND...

HECK! A SHERIFF!

FRESNO SET DOWN THE COFFEE POT AND WITH HIS GUN COCKED, HE STARTED TO SLINK AFTER BUCK...

SILENT AS A SHADOW, HE DOGGED THE SHERIFF STEALTHILY TILL BUCK PAUSED TO TIE UP HIS HORSE...

I'LL GO IT ALONE FROM HERE, BOY. THAT GROUND'S PRETTY HARD AND YOU'RE A MITE HEAVY-FOOTED, AND WE DON'T WANT TO SCARE OFF THAT BRACE OF BUZZARDS...

HOLD IT, MISTER!

BUCK STIFFENED. THEN MADE AS IF TO SWING ROUND. FRESNO PROMPTLY RAPPED OUT A WARNING IN A VOICE EDGED WITH MENACE...

KEEP YOUR BACK TO ME! THERE'S A FORTY-FIVE LINED UP ON YOU! LET GO THAT IRON OF YOURS AND UNBUCKLE YOUR GUNBELT!

BROPHY LAID THE SKILLET ASIDE AND FILLED HIS FIST WITH A SIX-SHOOTER. THE FLASH OF ITS BARREL IN THE SUNLIGHT MATCHED THE UGLY GLINT THAT SPARKED IN HIS NARROW EYES...

LONG TIME NO SEE, JONES — NOT SINCE YOU HAD US SENT UP FOR A STRETCH A FEW YEARS BACK. WHAT'S ON YOUR MIND? WE AIN'T BEEN IN ARIZONA FROM THE DAY WE WAS TURNED LOOSE. YOU'VE GOT NOTHING ON US NOW!

YOU BOTH GUNNED DOWN A PEACE OFFICER IN CALIFORNIA LESS THAN A WEEK AGO. HE HAPPENED TO BE A UNITED STATES' MARSHAL! THAT MEANS YOU'RE WANTED CLEAR ACROSS THE COUNTRY ON A FEDERAL CHARGE!

YEAH? AND WHAT DO YOU FIGURE YOU CAN DO ABOUT IT?

BROPHY TRIED TO CUT LOOSE WITH HIS COLT, BUT ROSS BEAT HIM TO THE TRIGGER. A BULLET SLAMMED INTO BROPHY'S SHOULDER WITH A JOLT THAT KNOCKED HIM SPRAWLING...

FRESNO'S GUN BARKED SAVAGELY A SPLIT-SECOND AFTER. HIS SHOT WAS MEANT TO KILL, BUT IT STRUCK THE BARREL OF YOUNG ARMSTRONG'S PISTOL AND SPUN THE WEAPON FROM HIS GRASP...

BEFORE FRESNO COULD LET GO WITH A SECOND SLUG BUCK WAS INSIDE HITTING-DISTANCE... HIS FIST FLASHED TO THE OUTLAW'S HEAD, SPINNING HIM ROUND...

FRESNO CRASHED BACKWARDS INTO A TANGLE OF THORNY UNDERGROWTH...

HEAD SINGING, HAND TO HEAD, FRESNO PEELED OUT OF THE THORN-PATCH AND SURGED TO HIS FEET, HE TOOK ONE SQUINT AT BUCK MOVING IN ON HIM AND RAN...

OKAY, ROSS! I'LL SEE HE DON'T GET FAR! YOU TAKE CARE OF BROPHY...

IT LOOKED LIKE ROSS DIDN'T HAVE A CHANCE OF MAKING A PLAY. HE WOULD NOT HAVE HAD A GHOST OF A CHANCE IF BROPHY HAD NOT BEEN HANDICAPPED HIMSELF. AS IT WAS, BOTH GUNS BLAZED IN UNISON.

THE DEPUTY SWAYED FORWARD, AND PITCHED FACE-DOWN. BROPHY LET OUT A STRANGLED CROAK AND SLUMPED IN A HEAP...

ONE GLANCE AT BROPHY WAS ENOUGH TO TELL BUCK THE OUTLAW HAD CASHED IN. ANOTHER MOMENT AND THE SHERIFF WAS CHECKING UP ANXIOUSLY ON ROSS ARMSTRONG

CREASED — THAT'S ALL, ROSS. YOU MUST BE THE LUCKIEST MAN IN ARIZONA RIGHT NOW...NO, THE SECOND LUCKIEST. IF YOU HADN'T SHOWED UP WHEN YOU DID, I WOULDN'T BE ALIVE MYSELF!

AFTER FIFTEEN MINUTES, WHEN ROSS HAD COME TO AND WAS ON HIS FEET AGAIN...

I'LL GO ON THE PROD FOR FRESNO, ROSS. YOU STAY HERE AND KEEP YOUR EYES SKINNED IN CASE HE CIRCLES BACK TO TRY FOR HIS PONY.

IT WAS A PROFITLESS TASK BUCK HAD SET HIMSELF, THOUGH...

CAN'T SEE HIDE NOR HAIR OF HIM — AND I DOUBT IF I'M LIKELY TO, IN THIS UNDERGROWTH. TROUBLE IS, HE COULD BE HOLED UP NO FURTHER THAN A ROPE'S LENGTH FROM ME AND STILL BE OUT OF SIGHT!

THE DEPUTY MADE A WRY FACE...

I'LL ADMIT MY RIGHT HAND AIN'T MUCH GOOD WHEN GUN-PLAY'S CALLED FOR, BUCK. IT DON'T COME NATURALLY TO ME TO USE IT. BUT I'LL KEEP PRACTISING, AND BEFORE I'M THROUGH IT'LL MEASURE UP TO MY LEFT!

SHORTLY AFTERWARDS HE AND BUCK HEADED NORTH AGAIN...WITH BROPHY. ALKALI CITY WAS BUCK'S DESTINATION. A PLOT OF GROUND ON BOOT HILL OUTSIDE THE TOWN WAS BROPHY'S. AS FOR ROSS, HE HAD ANOTHER ROAD TO TRAVEL...

WELL, THIS IS WHERE WE PART COMPANY, BUCK. BUT BEFORE WE DO, I WANT TO THANK YOU FOR ALL YOU'VE TAUGHT ME OVER THE LAST SIX MONTHS!

FORGET IT. IF YOU OWED ME ANYTHING, YOU EVENED UP THE SCORE TODAY ON OUR LAST ASSIGNMENT TOGETHER...WHEN YOU STOPPED BROPHY FROM BLOWING DAYLIGHT THROUGH ME!

SOCORRO NVA. MEXICO

ALKALI

Chapter 2. TRAIL TO SHOTGUN

EASTWARD TO SOCORRO, NEW MEXICO...ACROSS THE RIO GRANDE... SOUTHWARD OVER THE GUADALOUPE MOUNTAINS...AND ON INTO TEXAS WHERE MEN WERE SCHOOLED FROM BOYHOOD IN THE USE OF A GUN. THAT WAS THE ROUTE ROSS ARMSTRONG FOLLOWED...

THOSE DROVERS SURE SEEM TO BE IN AN ALL-FIRED HURRY. THE WAY THEY'RE HUSTLING THAT STOCK, I'D SAY THEY DON'T KNOW THEIR TRADE

HE HAD COME THROUGH LAND STRICKEN BY DROUGHT. NOW HE WAS IN A REGION THAT WAS DESERT ALL THE YEAR ROUND, FETLOCK-DEEP IN CRAWLING SANDS THAT THE HOT WINDS LIFTED INTO "DEVIL-WITCH" SPIRALS...

HEY, DUTCH— SMOKY— WE GOT COMPANY!

ROSS CAUGHT UP WITH THE DROVE THAT HAD BEEN CROSSING THE DESERT IN ADVANCE OF HIM. HE HAD NEVER SEEN A MUSTER OF SORRIER-LOOKING BEASTS — SO STARVED. THEIR HIDES HUNG SLACK OVER THEIR BONES...

HOWDY, FRIEND. YOU'RE TRAVELLING PRETTY FAST FOR HERDERS, AIN'T YOU? YOUR BEASTS ARE MIGHTY SHORT OF FAT AS IT IS, BUT I'M FIGURING THEY WON'T HAVE AN OUNCE OF TALLOW LEFT ON 'EM IF YOU HOLD THIS PACE.

YOU DON'T SAY? AND WHAT'S IT TO YOU, STRANGER?

THE TAIL-RIDER FOR THE GATHER OF CATTLE HAD SPOKEN GRUFFLY, UNFRIENDLY. THE TWO FLANK MEN WHO DROPPED BACK TO JOIN HIM WERE NO MORE AMIABLE...

DID WE HEAR A-RIGHT, SHAD? IS THIS HOMBRE TRYING TO TELL US HOW TO HANDLE A BUNCH OF STEERS?

NO OFFENCE INTENDED. I WAS ONLY OFFERING A PIECE OF ADVICE. I CAN SEE IT AIN'T WANTED, SO I'LL SHOVE ON.

YEAH, DO THAT, WILL YOU?

ROSS SPURRED AHEAD. MAYBE HE HAD TALKED OUT OF TURN BUT HE STILL RECKONED THOSE THREE MEN DID NOT KNOW THEIR BUSINESS. BUT HE WAS WRONG. SHAD BASSET, SMOKY COLLINS AND DUTCH KESSLER KNEW THEIR BUSINESS...

YOU DON'T SUPPOSE THAT SMART-ALECK GUESSED WHY WE WAS DRIVING THE HERD SO HARD?

NAW! HE'S JUST SOME BRASH KID THAT TOOK US FOR GREENHORNS!

COME EVENING, ROSS WAS CLEAR OF THE DESERT AND IN A COUNTRY OF LUSH HILLS AND VALLEYS...AND TWENTY-FOUR HOURS LATER HE REACHED HIS LONG JOURNEY'S END...

WELCOME TO SHOTGUN CITY

SHOTGUN CITY, PRINCIPAL TOWN IN MATADOR COUNTY, WAS A PEACEFUL TOWN IN SPITE OF ITS NAME, THOUGH IT HAD ONCE KNOWN TROUBLE. BUT THAT HAD BEEN BEFORE VINCE BRADY WAS INSTALLED AS SHERIFF...

WHO DO YOU SUPPOSE THAT YOUNG FELLER IS, SHERIFF?

COULD BE THE NEW DEPUTY I'M EXPECTING. HE'S DUE ANY DAY NOW.

ROSS DISMOUNTED IN FRONT OF THE SHERIFF'S OFFICE AND INTRODUCED HIMSELF. A BIG HAND CLOSED ON THE NEW DEPUTY'S...

GLAD TO MAKE YOUR ACQUAINTANCE. LET'S SEE, ROSS IS YOUR FIRST NAME, AIN'T IT? · OKAY, MINE'S VINCE! LET'S YOU AND ME START OFF ON THE RIGHT FOOT AS ROSS AND VINCE FROM NOW ON.

ROSS LIKED WHAT HE SAW—A MAN OF ACTION, FOR SURE...TOUGH AS THE SNAKESKIN BAND AROUND HIS HAT...

I'VE FIXED ACCOMODATION FOR YOU IN A ROOMING-HOUSE. THERE'S A STALL READY FOR YOUR HORSE IN THE LIVERY STABLE.

FIRST OFF, THOUGH, I'D LIKE YOU TO MEET POP DRISCOLL. POP LOOKS AFTER THE JAIL AT NIGHTS. USED TO BE A HARD-RIDING, FAST-SHOOTING DEPUTY HIMSELF— ONLY HE'S TOO LONG IN THE TOOTH FOR THAT NOW.

TOO LONG IN THE TOOTH! THAT'S A GOOD ONE. DANG ME IF I GOT SO MUCH AS THE STUMP OF A FANG LEFT IN MY HEAD!

ROSS HAD A VAGUE IMPRESSION HE HAD ENCOUNTERED THE MAYOR BEFORE, THOUGH HE COULD NOT REMEMBER THE OCCASION...

AIN'T YOU AND I MET SOME PLACE, YOUR HONOUR?

NOT TO MY RECOLLECTION.

ROSS DECIDED HE MUST BE MISTAKEN. BUT NEXT MORNING, WHEN HE REPORTED FOR DUTY HE AGAIN EXPERIENCED THE FEELING THAT GROGAN WAS NO STRANGER TO HIM...

I'LL SWEAR I KNOW THE MAYOR'S FACE, BUT I'M HANGED IF I CAN PLACE HIM, HE SEEMS KIND OF HET-UP. WONDER WHAT'S ON HIS MIND?

HAVE YOU SEEN THE SHERIFF, ARMSTRONG? HE'S NOT IN HIS OFFICE, AND I'VE GOT TO GET HOLD OF HIM RIGHT AWAY.

ON THE PORCH OF THE SHERIFF'S OFFICE, ROSS ARMSTRONG WAS QUICK TO IDENTIFY THE DROVERS HE HAD OVERHAULED IN THE DESERT AWAY TO THE NORTH-WEST...

I KNOW THOSE BIRDS! I RAN ACROSS 'EM WHILE THEY WERE RIDING HERD ON A BIG BUNCH OF STEERS.

YEAH? THEN YOU CAN BET THEY DIDN'T COME BY THOSE STEERS HONESTLY...NOT BASSETT, KESSLER AND COLLINS. RUSTLING'S THEIR SPECIALITY...

ROSS FLEXED HIS LEFT HAND AND SIDLED DOWN FROM THE PORCH, BENT ON CHALLENGING THE OUTLAWS. HE DID NOT HAVE TO. A LONG-LIMBED FIGURE STEPPED SUDDENLY INTO VIEW FROM SHOTGUN CITY'S COURT-HOUSE...

WOULD YOU FELLERS BE LOOKING FOR ME?

AS THE THREE MEN RAISED THEIR HANDS, JUDGE MORRIS SPOKE...

YOU THREE HAVE BEEN PLAGUING THE NEIGHBOURING COUNTIES FOR QUITE A SPELL. I GUESS YOU WERE FIXING TO DO THE SAME IN THIS ONE, OR DID YOU COUNT ON ADDING TO YOUR REPUTATIONS BY PICKING ON OUR SHERIFF?

THAT'S ABOUT THE SIZE OF IT, JUDGE. A MAN AS CELEBRATED AS VINCE IS A MARK FOR EVERY GUN TOTING BOASTER IN TEXAS—THOUGH IT'S A LONG TIME SINCE ANY OF THEIR KIND WORKED UP ENOUGH NERVE TO TRY AND CALL HIM OUT.

JUDGE MORRIS SHOWED HIMSELF TO BE A MAN OF ACTION...

WE'LL DEAL WITH THESE MEN WITHOUT DELAY, SHERIFF. CARRY OUT THE USUAL FORMALITIES AND PRODUCE THE ACCUSED BEFORE ME IN HALF-AN-HOUR'S TIME. I'LL HAVE MY CLERK MAKE THE NECESSARY ARRANGEMENTS FOR CONVENING THE COURT.

VINCE STRODE OFF WITH HIS CAPTIVES, AND THE CITIZENS STARTED TO DISPERSE...

'TAIN'T NO USE TRYING TO BUTTONHOLE VINCE WHEN HE'S MADE UP HIS MIND HE'S TOO BUSY TO HEAR YOU OUT, YOUNG FELLER. HE'S THE FINEST PEACE OFFICER MATADOR COUNTY EVER HAD, BUT I WOULDN'T CALL HIM A PATIENT MAN.

I BELIEVE I KNOW WHAT YOU WERE SO KEEN TO TELL HIM, ARMSTRONG. YOU WANTED TO TELL HIM ABOUT THE CATTLE THOSE THREE MEN WERE HERDING WHEN YOU SAW THEM. WELL, THEY PROBABLY SOLD 'EM BEFORE THEY DRIFTED IN HERE.

ROSS DID NOT THINK SO AND HE RECKONED GROGAN WOULDN'T HAVE THOUGHT SO EITHER, IF HE HAD SEEN HOW SCRAWNY THAT BUNCH OF BEEVES HAD BEEN...

I DOUBT THAT, MISTER MAYOR. I'VE A HUNCH I MIGHT LOCATE 'EM. IF I DO, VINCE WILL ONLY HAVE TO SEND WORD TO THE RANCHER WHOSE BRAND THEY CARRY AND THEY CAN BE ROUNDED UP. MEANTIME, I'D BE OBLIGED IF YOU'D GIVE THE SHERIFF A MESSAGE FROM ME THE FIRST CHANCE YOU GET.

ROSS THEN COLLECTED HIS HORSE AND LEFT TOWN. HE WAS WELL ON HIS WAY WHEN BASSET, KESSLER AND COLLINS WERE BROUGHT BEFORE JUDGE MORRIS...

HEAR YE! HEAR YE! THIS COURT IS NOW IN SESSION...

THE CASE WAS CUT-AND-DRIED. IT ENDED IN THE JUDGE IMPOSING A TWELVE MONTHS' SENTENCE... A SENTENCE ACCEPTABLE TO THE PRISONERS, HAD THE COMMUNITY OF SHOTGUN BUT KNOWN IT...

IT'S ALL PANNING OUT FINE AND DANDY.

YOU SAID IT, SHAD.

YEAH, FROM NOW ON WE'LL BE SITTING PRETTY...

SILENCE IN COURT! CUT OUT THAT MUTTERING!

THE OUTLAWS WERE ESCORTED TO A JAIL BEHIND THE SHERIFF'S OFFICE, WHERE OTHERS OF THEIR BREED ALREADY OCCUPIED CELLS. ABOUT THAT SAME TIME, ROSS ARMSTRONG WAS RIDING PAST AN OUTLYING RANCH-HOUSE...

PRIME BEEF-CATTLE, NOT LIKE THE CRITTERS I HOPE TO TRACK DOWN. BUT IF I'M RIGHT THE STEERS THAT WERE RUSTLED ARE ON SOME SUCH GRAZING-GROUND AS THIS — WHERE THEY COULD BE FATTENED UP TILL THEY'D FETCH TOP PRICES FROM A BUYER WHO WOULDN'T ASK QUESTIONS.

HE WAS MAKING FOR THE HILLS THAT FRINGED THE DESERT, THEY MARKED THE NORTH-WEST LIMITS OF MATADOR COUNTY. TRAVELLING AT A FAST CLIP MOST OF THE WAY, HE REACHED THEM IN THE EARLY AFTERNOON, BUT HAD TO ROAM FAR AND WIDE BEFORE HE FOUND WHAT HE WAS SEEKING...

THAT'S THE HERD ALL RIGHT. I WONDER WHO THIS RANGE BELONGS TO — IF IT BELONGS TO ANYBODY ?

HE WAS IMMEDIATELY CUT SHORT BY THE BLINDING FLASH AND DEAFENING ROAR OF A SCATTER-GUN. A GASPING CRY BROKE FROM HIM AS ITS DEADLY CHARGE STRUCK HIM FULL IN THE CHEST...

AAAARGH!

SPOOKED BY THE SHOTGUN'S EXPLOSION, THE CATTLE IN THE VALLEY BAWLED WITH FRIGHT. BUT ROSS ARMSTRONG DID NOT HEAR THEM. HE WAS DEAD... KILLED BY AN UNKNOWN HAND...

Chapter 3. DOUBLE-HARNESS

A WEEK LATER BUCK JONES SHOWED UP IN AUSTIN, TEXAS, AT THE HOME OF TOBIAS HALDANE, ATTORNEY-GENERAL FOR THAT STATE...

IT'S SURE GOOD TO SEE YOU, BUCK. DID I UNDERSTAND YOU TO SAY YOU'RE ON A MONTH'S LEAVE OF DUTY?

I AM, TOBE. I'M HERE BECAUSE I'D LIKE TO KNOW THE CIRCUMSTANCES CONNECTED WITH THE MURDER OF A YOUNG DEPUTY CALLED ROSS ARMSTRONG.

THEY HAD A LONG ACQUAINTANCE, BUCK JONES AND TOBE HALDANE, AND THE THOUSAND MILES THAT LAY BETWEEN ALKALI AND AUSTIN HAD NOT DIMMED THEIR REGARD FOR EACH OTHER...

I HEARD OF YOUNG ARMSTRONG'S DEATH JUST BEFORE I WAS DUE TO GO ON LEAVE. I WASN'T ABLE TO LEARN ANY DETAILS, THOUGH. THAT'S WHY I DECIDED TO MAKE THE JOURNEY TO AUSTIN AND LOOK YOU UP, TOBE.

THE ATTORNEY-GENERAL RELATED ALL HE KNEW... AND INDICATED THERE WERE DARK AND SINISTER INFLUENCES OPERATING IN MATADOR COUNTY...

IT'S A MYSTERY, BUCK. MATADOR HAS THE LEAST CRIME IN TEXAS, YET THREE DEPUTIES IN A ROW HAVE BEEN GUNNED DOWN — WITH NO CLUE AS TO THE IDENTITY OF THEIR KILLER.

THREE IN A ROW, EH? IT SOUNDS LIKE MATADOR COUNTY IS WELL-NAMED...

MATADOR...THE WORD COULD MEAN BULLFIGHTER BUT IT COULD ALSO MEAN KILLER — AND THAT WAS WHAT IT HAD MEANT FOR THREE ILL-FATED PEACE OFFICERS...

THEY WERE ALL YOUNG MEN, BUCK. I WISH I COULD GIVE VINCE BRADY SOMEBODY OF YOUR CALIBRE. SOMEBODY TO HELP HIM FIND OUT WHY THOSE DEPUTIES DIED AND WHO MURDERED THEM.

WHY NOT? I'D BE WILLING TO FOREGO MY LEAVE. BRADY AND I MIGHT BE ABLE TO UNCOVER WHAT'S GOING ON DOWN THERE.

A WINCHESTER REPEATER SPAT FLAME, AND BULLETS SNAPPED CLOSE. INSTANTLY VINCE BRADY SNATCHED HIS RIFLE FROM ITS SHEATH, AND FISHED OUT A BANDOLIER OF CARTRIDGES FOR IT FROM A SADDLE-BAG.

GRAB THESE AND GIVE ME COVERING FIRE, BUCK!

BRADY DID NOT WAIT FOR AN ARGUMENT. HE HOOKED HIS HEELS INTO HIS HORSE AND WENT STRAIGHT FOR THE HUT AT A DEAD RUN. BUCK PROMPTLY SWUNG ASIDE, PEELED OUT OF THE SADDLE AND DROPPED DOWN ON ONE KNEE...

COVERING FIRE, HUH? IF EVER A MAN NEEDED IT, VINCE BRADY DOES! HE'S TAKING A HECK OF A CHANCE!

BOWERS AND CRANE DUCKED INTO THE SHACK AND OPENED UP ON VINCE FROM A WINDOW. BUCK SLAPPED OFF SHOT AFTER SHOT—AND QUICKLY REALISED THAT THE WEAPON IN HIS HANDS WAS JUST ABOUT USELESS...

WHAT IN TARNATION'S WRONG WITH THIS RIFLE! IT'S CLEAN OFF THE AIM!

HIS BULLETS WERE STRIKING WIDE AND HIGH...

WE GOT NOTHING TO FEAR FROM THAT HOMBRE WITH THE SHOULDER-GUN, CURLY.

WITH DISGUST, BUCK FLUNG THE RIFLE ASIDE AND SWUNG ON TO HIS HORSE. HE HAD TO GO IN CLOSE TO HELP VINCE, NOW—AND HE HAD TO MOVE FAST...

BUT POP MADE NO SUSPICIOUS MOVE WITH ANY OF THE FIREARMS. BUCK WAITED TILL THE OLD FELLOW HAD REPLACED THEM, AND THEN LEFT THE JAILER TO HIS LONELY VIGIL...

GOOD EVENING, JONES.

EVENING, JUDGE.

JUDGE MORRIS WAS A FRIENDLY SOUL. NOT ONE TO STAND ON CEREMONY — EXCEPT IN THE COURT-HOUSE, WHERE HE HAD LAST SENTENCED BOWERS AND CRANE. HE DROPPED IN NOW ON POP...

DON'T GET UP, DRISCOLL. I JUST THOUGHT I'D JOIN YOU IN A COFFEE...

SURE, JUDGE, COME ON IN!

THE JUDGE STAYED GOSSIPING FOR A COUPLE OF HOURS. AS HE LEFT...

THERE'S NOTHING UPPETY ABOUT JUDGE MORRIS, THAT'S FOR SURE. BY GOLLY, THERE AIN'T MANY MEN IN HIS POSITION WOULD BOTHER TO BE SOCIABLE WITH A NOBODY LIKE ME.

SHOTGUN CITY WAS STILL AND QUIET. ITS CITIZENS ALL ASLEEP, AS WAS POP DRISCOLL, THE ONE MAN WHO SHOULD HAVE BEEN WIDE AWAKE. TO THE EARS OF THE INHABITANTS OF TWO CELLS IN VINCE BRADY'S JAIL, POP'S SNORING WAS MUSIC...

COME ON, BOYS! DRISCOLL'S SO DEEP IN DREAMLAND YOU COULD SET HIS WHISKERS ALIGHT AND HE WOULDN'T RAISE A BLEAT!

THE OUTLAWS CLOSED THE DOORS OF THEIR CELLS AND LET THEMSELVES OUT OF THE BUILDING BY A BACK EXIT...

THEY CREPT TO A BARN SOME DISTANCE OFF. HERE THE HORSES, SADDLERY AND GUNS OF PRISONERS WERE KEPT PENDING THEIR OFFICIAL RELEASE. THIS BAND OF JAILBIRDS MADE UNOFFICIAL USE OF THEM NOW...

WE'LL CAT-FOOT DOWN INTO THE BED OF THIS SHALLOW CREEK AND WORK NORTH TILL IT'S SAFE TO MOUNT UP AND RIDE. OUT AND BACK, WE HAVE TO TAKE CARE WE DON'T RAISE AN ALARM.

OKAY, MADDOX, WE GET THE IDEA.

WHEN AT LAST THEY FORKED THEIR SADDLES THEY SPURRED THROUGH THE GLOOM TILL THEY WERE WELL ACROSS THE COUNTY BOUNDARY. A RIDGE-TOP ABOVE A RIBBON OF TRAIL WAS THEIR HALTING-PLACE ... AN OVERNIGHT SOUTH-BOUND STAGE THEIR TARGET.

THERE SHE COMES NOW. I HOPE SHE'S TOTING TEN THOUSAND DOLLARS IN BANKNOTES LIKE WE WAS TOLD.

YOU CAN DEPEND ON IT, BASSETT. YOU SHOULD KNOW BETTER THAN TO DOUBT THE WORD OF SOMEBODY THAT HAS WAYS AND MEANS OF FINDING OUT ALL ABOUT BANK SHIPMENTS.

THE COACH'S SIX-HORSE TEAM SWERVED WILDLY OUT OF CONTROL UNDER A BLIZZARD OF LEAD FROM THE OUTLAWS' FORTY-FIVES. THE VEHICLE BUCKETED OFF THE TRAIL ON TWO WHEELS AND KEELED OVER...

IT CRASHED IN A BOIL OF DUST. DRIVER AND GUARD LAY WHERE THEY FELL. THEY REMAINED INERT AND STUNNED WHILE SHOTGUN CITY'S TRUANT JAILBIRDS POUNCED ON THE STRONG-BOX THE STAGE HAD CARRIED...

THE BOX WAS PLUNDERED OF ITS CONTENTS. THE GANG MADE OFF WITH THEIR LOOT. BEFORE DAWN THEY WERE IN THE CELL-ROW OF SHOTGUN CITY'S CALABOOSE AGAIN— WITH THEIR HARDWARE, HORSES AND SADDLERY BACK IN THE BARN FROM WHICH THEY HAD COLLECTED THEM...

A GOOD NIGHT'S WORK AND EVERY MAN OF US WITH A CAST-IRON ALIBI!

POP DRISCOLL WAS FAST ASLEEP. HE WOKE TO FIND THE SUNLIGHT STREAMING THROUGH THE WINDOWS, AND HE GREETED IT WITH A SHAMEFACED AIR...

IT'S BROAD DAY! THERE'S CONNOLLY ON THE WAY TO HIS BANK— AND RITTER OPENING UP HIS STORE! I MUST'VE DOZED THE WHOLE NIGHT THROUGH! 'TAIN'T THE FIRST TIME IT'S HAPPENED NEITHER, NOT BY A LONG CHALK. IF I DON'T STAY ON MY TOES I'LL LOSE MY JOB...

Chapter 4. ALIAS FRESNO

BUCK HEARD OF THE STAGE-COACH ROBBERY LATER IN THE DAY WHILE AWAITING VINCE'S RETURN. BECAUSE IT HAD HAPPENED NOT FAR FROM MATADOR'S WESTERN BOUNDARY, HE UNDERTOOK A PATROL ON THE OFF-CHANCE THE CULPRITS MIGHT BE SKULKING ON HIS SIDE OF THE LINE...

THESE COULD BE THE TRACKS OF THE BANDITS. IF SO, THERE'S NO SIGN THEY CAME OUT ON THE OTHER SIDE, WHICH MEANS THEY KEPT TO THE WATER AND SWUNG NORTH OR SOUTH. MY GUESS IS THEY WENT NORTH. SOUTH WOULD SURELY BRING 'EM TOO CLOSE TO SHOTGUN CITY FOR THEIR COMFORT.

HE FOLLOWED THE CREEK NORTHWARD IN THE HOPE OF DISCOVERING THE CONTINUATION OF THOSE TRACKS. NOT TILL SUNDOWN DID HE ABANDON HIS FUTILE QUEST. HE STARTED BACK FOR SHOTGUN BY THE TRAIL THAT LED PAST THE ANDREWS' PLACE...

HECK! WHAT'S THAT KID UP TO?

FRE

SO MAYOR GROGAN AND FRESNO WERE BROTHERS, ALIKE IN FACE AND FIGURE THOUGH CLEARLY FAR APART IN CHARACTER. FROM HIS VANTAGE-POINT BUCK SAW FRESNO PRODUCE SOMETHING FROM HIS PANTS' HIP-POCKET — SAW THE MAYOR SCRUTINISE IT AND HEARD HIM UTTER AN EXCLAMATION...

THE NAME WRITTEN ON THIS ENVELOPE SURPRISES YOU, HUH? YEAH, I THOUGHT IT WOULD, BUT I FIGURE I CAN DO A DEAL WITH THE GENT IN QUESTION.

WHAT KIND OF A DEAL? WHAT POSSIBLE BUSINESS COULD *YOU* HAVE WITH A MAN LIKE *HIM*?

FRESNO BECAME EVASIVE — GAVE ONLY A HINT OF WHAT WAS IN HIS MIND...

LET'S JUST SAY I CAN SPILL THE BEANS ABOUT A RACKET IN OPERATION HERE, BUT THAT DON'T CONCERN YOU NONE. YOU DELIVER THE NOTE TO WHO IT'S INTENDED FOR, TIE IT TO A ROCK AND TOSS IT THROUGH HIS WINDOW. THEN YOU WON'T BE CONNECTED WITH ME AND THE PRECIOUS FAMILY NAME WILL STAY PROTECTED. AND SO WILL YOU*!*

HITCHING HIS PONY, BUCK STOLE AFTER THE WANTED MAN— FOLLOWED HIM THROUGH THE GLOOM TILL HE SAW HIM HUMP DOWN BY THE EDGE OF THE CREEK THAT FLOWED NEAR SHOTGUN CITY...

TIME DRAGGED BY, TILL HURRIED FOOTSTEPS ALERTED FRESNO — AND BUCK AS WELL. A FIGURE SHOWED UP IN THE DARK, A PORTLY FIGURE HASTENING ALONG THE WATER'S EDGE...

JUDGE MORRIS?

YES, I'M JUDGE MORRIS. WHAT'S THE IDEA, BUSTING MY STUDY WINDOW? AND WHAT'S THE MEANING OF THIS NOTE? IT DON'T MAKE SENSE TO ME. WHAT'S IT ALL ABOUT?

FRESNO DIDN'T ENLIGHTEN HIM ON THE SUBJECT OF THE BROKEN WINDOW. BUT HE WAS SPECIFIC AS TO THE MEANING OF THE NOTE...

COME OFF IT, JUDGE. I KNOW YOU'RE IN CAHOOTS WITH OUTLAWS FROM BEYOND THIS COUNTY'S BOUNDARIES. I KNOW THAT WHEN THINGS GET TOO HOT FOR 'EM THEY SLIP ACROSS HERE AND GET THEMSELVES ARRESTED. AND I KNOW WHEN YOU SENTENCE 'EM THEY'RE GIVEN THE KEYS TO THE JAIL.

NO MAN COULD HAVE LOOKED MORE FIDGETY THAN THE JUDGE RIGHT THEN. HE BEGAN CHEWING AT HIS NAILS. HIS PLUMP FACE, EVEN IN THE GLOOM, SHOWED PALE...

FOR A START, THEM OUTLAWS MAKE A CASH-DOWN PAYMENT— OR TURN OVER RUSTLED LIVESTOCK THAT'S HELD ON LAND BELONGING TO YOU TILL YOU FIND A BUYER. AFTER THAT, YOUR ARRANGEMENT WITH 'EM IS RUN ON A PERCENTAGE BASIS...

YEAH, A PERCENTAGE BASIS. THEY SLIP OUT OF JAIL AT DEAD OF NIGHT WHENEVER THEY'VE BEEN TIPPED OFF THAT THERE'S EASY PICKINGS TO BE HAD. A SLEEPING-POWDER DROPPED INTO THE TURNKEY'S COFFEE BY YOU, AND THEY'RE ALL SET. YOU GET YOUR CUT OF THE LOOT, AND—

WHO TOLD YOU ALL THIS?

FRESNO LEERED AT MORRIS...

LET'S NOT MENTION NAMES, BUT IT SO HAPPENS I'M TEXAS-BORN, AND ONE I MET IN CALIFORNIA EXPLAINED YOU COULD BE A REAL FRIEND IN NEED IF EVER I WAS IN A JAM.

BUCK WAS TAKING IN EVERY WORD. SO WAS JUDGE MORRIS — AND HE WAS DENYING NOTHING... BUT ANOTHER WAS APPROACHING WITHIN EARSHOT, QUIETLY, OMINOUSLY...

ALL RIGHT, FRESNO. WHAT IS IT YOU WANT? BOARD AND LODGING IN THAT COSY LITTLE CALABOOSE?

ACCOMODATION IN THE COUNTY JAIL WAS NOT THE AIM OF WALT GROGAN, ALIAS FRESNO. HE HAD NOT MADE HIS LABORIOUS WAY HERE FOR SUCH A PURPOSE — COVERING THE LAST FEW HUNDRED MILES ON A STOLEN HORSE THAT HAD FINALLY DROPPED EXHAUSTED UNDER HIM...

YOUR COSY LITTLE CALABOOSE AIN'T NO PLACE FOR ME, JUDGE— NOT WITH A FEDERAL CHARGE PINNED ON ME. WHAT I WANT FROM YOU IS A HORSE THAT'LL GET ME TO MEXICO IN A HURRY—AND FIFTY THOUSAND DOLLARS SO I CAN LIVE THE REST OF MY DAYS ON EASY STREET.

UNAWARE HE WAS NOT THE ONLY ONE WHO WAS LISTENING TO FRESNO AND MORRIS, BUCK HEARD THE JUDGE SPLUTTER AN OUTRAGED RESPONSE...

YOU'RE OUT OF YOUR MIND IF YOU SUPPOSE I'D PAY YOU THAT MUCH...

YOU'D BETTER, JUDGE. IF YOU DON'T AND I GET CAUGHT, I'LL TALK. IT MIGHT SAVE MY NECK TO BLOW THE LID OFF YOUR LITTLE SET-UP.

JUDGE MORRIS HAD DRAWN BACK FROM FRESNO. SUDDENLY, UNEXPECTEDLY, HE THREW A GLANCE ALOFT...

GET HIM, VINCE! HE'S ALL YOURS!

FRESNO JERKED HIS HEAD UPWARD, HIS HAND FLASHED TO HIS HOLSTER, BUT BEFORE HIS FINGERS COULD CLOSE ON HIS GUN BUTT, VINCE BRADY'S GUN ROARED SHATTERINGLY...

AAAARGH!

TOO LATE, FRESNO DRAGGED HIS IRON CLEAR. HE FIRED AIMLESSLY, PUMPING LEAD SKYWARD AS HE REELED AWAY. A CHARGE FROM THE SECOND BARREL OF BRADY'S GUN STRUCK HIM AND HE SPUN AROUND AND PITCHED HEADLONG...

THAT HOMBRE THOUGHT HE HELD ALL THE ACES, JUDGE. WHAT HE DIDN'T SEEM TO KNOW WAS THAT YOU AND I WERE PARTNERS. AND HE SURE DIDN'T KNOW YOU'D GOT IN TOUCH WITH ME AS SOON AS YOU READ HIS MESSAGE.

WORDS TUMBLED FROM VINCE BRADY'S LIPS IN CROAKING PROTEST...

IT AIN'T SO, JONES! I NEVER GUNNED DOWN NO DEPUTIES! WHY, I TRIED TO SAVE ARMSTRONG. I HEARD FROM MAYOR GROGAN HE'D RODE OFF TO LOOK FOR SOME RUSTLED STEERS. I WENT AFTER HIM, BUT WAS JUST TOO LATE TO PREVENT HIM BEING KILLED BY AN OUTLAW ...

YEAH? TELL ME ABOUT IT, BRADY.

BRADY BABBLED ON. HE WAS NO LONGER THE FLAMBOYANT MAN OF ACTION WHOSE NAME WAS A BYWORD FOR RECKLESS COURAGE IN MATADOR COUNTY...

I SAW ROSS CUT HIS RIGHT HAND DOWN TO HIS HOLSTER, BUT THE OTHER MAN LET HIM HAVE IT WITH A SHOTGUN AND THEN TOOK OFF. POOR ROSS, HE WAS FAST WITH THAT RIGHT HAND OF HIS, BUT HE DIDN'T HAVE A CHANCE —

BUCK BROKE IN ON HIM. HE HAD HEARD ENOUGH — ENOUGH TO BE CERTAIN BRADY WAS LYING. IF BRADY HAD EVER SEEN ROSS DRAW, HE WOULD HAVE KNOWN AS WELL AS BUCK THAT ROSS WOULD NOT HAVE USED HIS RIGHT HAND...

YOU STICK TO THAT YARN, BRADY. SURE, YOU STICK TO IT. IT'LL BE GOOD ENOUGH TO HANG YOU...AND THE JUDGE TOO — AS AN ACCESSORY...

JUDGE MORRIS SPOKE THEN, IN A TONE FALSETTO WITH FEAR...

I HAD NOTHING TO DO WITH ANY KILLINGS, JONES! I WAS ALL AGAINST THEM! BRADY WAS RESPONSIBLE FOR THEM—AND THAT'S THE TRUTH! I'LL TURN STATE'S EVIDENCE, SO HELP ME —

YOU TWO-TIMING RAT!

BUCK HAULED BRADY FROM HIS KNEES AND THRUST BOTH HIS PRISONERS TOWARDS THE SLOPE...

YOUR SHERIFF AND THE JUDGE ARE BOTH LOW-DOWN CROOKS, FRIENDS...PARTNERS IN A SET-UP THAT DIDN'T DRAW THE LINE AT MURDER...BUT YOU'LL BE HEARING ALL THE FACTS CONCERNING THEM WHEN THEY STAND TRIAL...

WHO'S THAT DOWN THAT AT THE WATER'S EDGE, JONES?

THE MAYOR WAS POINTING WITH A TREMULOUS HAND TO THE BODY OF BRADY'S LAST VICTIM. BUCK COULD HAVE GIVEN THAT VICTIM A NAME THAT WOULD HAVE SET SHOTGUN CITY BY THE EARS. BUT HE DIDN'T... AS FAR AS HE WAS CONCERNED, THE NAME WOULD STAY PROTECTED...

HE'S NO ONE YOU'D KNOW, MISTER MAYOR... EXCEPT AS A FACE ON A REWARD-POSTER...A MAN CALLED FRESNO...

WHEN BUCK JONES LEFT MATADOR COUNTY, VINCE BRADY HAD PAID THE SUPREME PENALTY FOR HIS CRIMES AND MORRIS WAS BEGINNING A LIFE SENTENCE...

ALKALI CITY LAY A THOUSAND MILES AHEAD OF BUCK... AND CLOSE BEHIND HIM — SHOTGUN. A TOWN WITH NO DARK SECRETS NOW, NO TRUANT JAILBIRDS WHO RODE BY NIGHT. A TOWN THAT WAS A LAIR FOR THE LAWLESS NO LONGER...

Printed in England and published each month by Fleetway Publications Ltd., Fleetway House, Farringdon Street, London, E.C.4. Sole Agents: Australasia, Messrs. Gordon & Gotch, Ltd.; South Africa, Central News Agency, Ltd.; Federation of Rhodesia and Nyasaland, Messrs. Kingstons, Ltd. Cowboy Picture Library is sold subject to the following conditions, that it shall not, without the written consent of the Publishers first given, be lent, resold, hired out or otherwise disposed of by way of Trade except at the full retail price as shown on the cover; and that it shall not be lent, resold, hired out or otherwise disposed of in a mutilated condition, or in any unauthorised cover by way of Trade; or affixed to or as part of any publication or advertising, literary or pictorial matter whatsoever. SG

Davy Crockett—
RICAREE!

IN THE MOUNTAIN CAMP OF THE RICAREES, THE FOUR CHIEFS OF TRIBAL COUNCIL HAD ARGUED ENDLESSLY FOR MORE THAN SIX HOURS, CAJOLING, PERSUADING, DEMANDING...
THEIR TOPIC WAS WAR— THE CRIPPLING STRUGGLE ON THE SOUTHERN FRONTIER BETWEEN THE MASSIVE ARMIES OF THE UNITED STATES AND MEXICO...

I SAY STRIKE AT THE AMERICANS WHILST THEY ARE WEAKENED BY THE ATTACKS OF THE DARK-HAIRED ONES!

NO! I HAVE JOURNEYED TO THE LANDS OF THE DARK-HAIRED ONES, AND THEY ARE EVIL. THEY HATE THE RED MAN WITH BITTERNESS AND LOATHING.

AYE, IT IS SO! ALTHOUGH THE AMERICANS SOMETIMES BREAK THEIR TREATIES, WITH THE MEXICANS THERE WOULD BE NO TREATIES TO BREAK.

THERE WAS ANOTHER MAN PRESENT IN THE RICAREE CAMP—A MAN OF CRUEL AND RUTHLESS CUNNING—THE TRADER, JOSIAH CANNON! HIS FUTURE LIVELIHOOD DEPENDING UPON THE SALE OF FIREARMS TO A NATION ENGAGED IN WAR, CANNON CURLED HIS LIPS IN AN EVIL SNEER AS HE STOOD UP AND SMOOTHLY ADDRESSED THE COUNCIL...

NOW SEE HERE! I'M YOUR FRIEND, AND I CAN ADVISE YOU WELL. BLACK KETTLE'S RIGHT, YOU'LL COLLECT THE BIGGEST HAUL O' LOOT AN' SCALPS YOU'VE EVER DREAMED OF, IF YOU TAKE A SMACK AT THE PALEFACE SOLDIERS NOW. YOU CAN ATTEND TO THE MEXICANS LATER—YOU'RE WARRIORS AIN'T YOU? OR MAYBE YOU'RE SQUAWS...

CANNON'S SLY TAUNT RAISED LOW GROWLS OF ANGER FROM THE SURROUNDING RICAREES, BUT THE THREE CHIEFS REMAINED UNSWAYED

THE RICAREES ARE NOT SQUAWS—BUT NEITHER ARE THEY FOOLS. ONE MOUTH ONLY OF THE COUNCIL SPEAKS FOR WAR AGAINST THE PALEFACES, AND THOUGH IT IS THAT OF THE HEAD CHIEF, HIS WORDS CANNOT PREVAIL AGAINST THE REST OF THE TRIBAL CEADERS. MY TWO BROTHERS AND I COUNSEL THAT WE JOIN THE PALEFACES AND DRIVE BACK THE DARK-HAIRED ONES

ALL EYES TURNED TO BLACK KETTLE, AWAITING HIS ANSWER HIS CHEST HEAVED IN A DEEP AND BITTER SIGH...

I CANNOT AGREE TO THIS THE COUNCIL MUST REMAIN DIVIDED, AND UNTIL ITS VOICES ARE AS ONE, THE RICAREES SHALL SIDE NEITHER WITH PALEFACE NOR DARK-HAIR THE MEETING IS FINISHED.

INWARDLY FURIOUS, JOSIAH CANNON COLLECTED HIS HORSE AND LEFT THE VILLAGE. SCARCELY HAD HE RIDDEN ONE MILE BEFORE HE STRUCK TROUBLE! A PATROL OF CAVALRY FROM NEARBY FORT GILLMAN, LED BY NONE OTHER THAN DAVY CROCKETT, SUDDENLY MATERIALISED FROM THE COVER OF SOME TRAILSIDE BRUSH!

WHA...?

HOLD IT, CANNON! YOU'RE UNDER ARREST! YOU'VE BEEN TRYING TO STIR UP TROUBLE WITH THE LOCAL TRIBES AND THAT'S A MIGHTY SERIOUS OFFENCE BAD LUCK FOR YOU THAT A SHAWNEE SUB-CHIEF TIPPED US OFF!

UNABLE TO RESIST, CANNON WAS TAKEN TO FORT GILLMAN AND FLUNG INTO A CELL TO AWAIT TRIAL...BUT THAT VERY NIGHT, WHEN ONLY THE SENTRIES OF THE GUARD WERE AWAKE...

YOU'D BETTER LEARN TO KEEP FURTHER AWAY FROM DESPERATE MEN LIKE ME, SUCKER!

THE GUARDROOM CELLS WERE SET AT THE CENTRE OF THE COMMAND POST OF THE FORT, AND TO GET OUT, THE RENEGADE TRADER HAD TO PASS THROUGH THE OFFICE OF THE GARRISON COMMANDER...

CANNON'S STOLEN PISTOL ROSE AND FELL IN A SILENT, SLASHING ARC, AND COLONEL STRONG PITCHED HEADLONG OVER THE PAPERS LITTERING HIS DESK!

HEY! WHAT'S THIS? BY HICKORY, THIS MESSAGE COULD MEAN A LOT TO BLACK KETTLE! YEAH, AN' I RECKON HE MIGHT GIVE ME A REAL HELPIN' HAND IN RETURN!

AND WITH AN EVIL SMIRK PLAYING ON HIS THIN LIPS, THE TREACHEROUS TRADER SLUNK FROM THE COMMAND POST AND SLIPPED SILENTLY OVER THE REAR WALL TO FREEDOM!

DAWN WAS ALREADY PAINTING THE EASTERN SKY WHEN COLONEL STRONG BEGAN TO GATHER HIS SCATTERED SENSES, BUT THE DISCOVERY OF CANNON'S ESCAPE, COUPLED WITH THE DISAPPEARANCE OF A VITAL AND SECRET DESPATCH, JERKED HIM FULLY ALERT WITHIN SECONDS!

ALARM! ALARM! TURN OUT THE GUARD!

IN A MATTER OF MINUTES, THE WHOLE FORT WAS SWARMING WITH LIFE AS SOLDIERS DASHED HITHER AND THITHER TO THEIR POSTS. IN THE COLONEL'S OFFICE, THE TENSION WAS AT FEVER PITCH!

BY HICKORY! SUPPOSING HE GOES TO THE RICAREES WITH IT!

THERE WAS A DESPATCH ON MY DESK— WARNING ME OF AN IMPENDING MEXICAN ATTACK! IT STATED WE COULD EXPECT A TOUGH TIME— WITH NO HOPE OF REINFORCEMENTS... GENTLEMEN, CANNON HAS THAT MESSAGE!

IF HE TAKES IT THERE, EVERY HOTHEAD IN THE TRIBE WILL KNOW WHERE TO STRIKE FOR A BELT-FULL OF EASY SCALPS AND QUICK LOOT WE'LL BE SUNK, AND SO WILL OUR COUNTRY WHEN THE MEXES BREAK THROUGH!

THEN THE TALL FIGURE IN FRONTIER BUCK-SKINS EASED HIMSELF COMFORTABLY ON THE MUZZLE OF HIS KENTUCKY LONG GUN, AND HIS EVEN DRAWL FELL LIKE DROPS OF OIL ON THE TROUBLED WATERS OF THE COMMANDANT'S OFFICE...

REST EASY, COLONEL. I'LL BRING HIM BACK, DOUBLE-QUICK IF AMERICA'S AT STAKE, THEN DAVY CROCKETT WON'T LET UP UNTIL THE VARMINT'S WELL OUT OF HARM'S WAY.

BRAVE WORDS, DAVY—I HOPE TO GLORY YOU'RE RIGHT!

WITHOUT WASTING A SECOND, DAVY SADDLED HIS HORSE AND GALLOPED FROM THE FORT THE TRADER'S TRAIL WAS AS CLEAR AS HAND-WRITING, BUT HE HAD TOO GREAT A START, AND IT WAS NOT UNTIL HE REACHED THE RICAREE CAMP THAT DAVY TRACKED HIS QUARRY DOWN...

GREETINGS, BEAR SLAYER. WHY DO YOU COME TO BLACK KETTLE'S LODGES ?

YOU'RE SHELTERING A WHITE RENEGADE, BLACK KETTLE —A WANTED MAN. I'VE COME TO TAKE HIM BACK TO JAIL.

A SCORNFUL SNEER ON HIS LIPS, JOSIAH CANNON CLIMBED TO HIS FEET AND THREW BACK HIS HEAD IN A MOCKING LAUGH..

HAW! CROCKETT, I'VE BEEN HERE JUST OVER AN HOUR—AND I'VE HAD PLENTY OF TIME TO MAKE SURE YOU CAN'T TAKE ME....

...MEET MOON FLOWER, MY WIFE!

IN ASTONISHED DISBELIEF, DAVY LOOKED FROM CANNON TO MOON FLOWER TO BLACK KETTLE IN ALL THEIR EYES WAS NOTHING BUT OPEN, MOCKING LAUGHTER...

IT IS TRUE. CANNON IS MY FRIEND, AND HE MARRIED MY DAUGHTER THIS MORNING. NOW HE IS RICAREE, AND ONLY A RICAREE CAN CAPTURE HIM WHAT SAY YOU TO THIS, BEAR SLAYER?

HEH! PICK YOURSELF A BRIDE CROCKETT! GO ON— GET MARRIED! HAW! HAW!

AS THE SLACK RAN OUT, DAVY STOPPED, DUG HIS HEELS IN, AND FLUNG HIS WHOLE MASSIVE WEIGHT AGAINST THE ROPES! HIS MUSCLES RIPPLING BENEATH HIS SUN-BRONZED SKIN, HE WRENCHED THE GALLOPING HORSES ROUND IN A TIGHT CIRCLE!

I'VE — DONE IT!

A GREAT SHOUT OF AWE WELLED UP FROM THE WATCHING RICAREES AS DAVY YANKED THE STAMPING MUSTANGS TO A HALT HE HAD WON THE FIRST TEST BY SKILL AND CUNNING AS WELL AS STRENGTH —AND HE HAD WON IT WELL!

NEXT TEST, BOYS. SPEED IT UP — I'M GETTING IMPATIENT!

AIEEEE! SEE THE MIGHT OF THE BEAR SLAYER!

THE SECOND TEST WAS NO LESS DANGEROUS THAN THE FIRST. HIS HANDS TIED SECURELY TOGETHER, DAVY WAS HURLED BODILY INTO A CASCADING MOUNTAIN TORRENT...

NOW REACH THE FAR SIDE, BEAR SLAYER— IF YOU CAN!

ROLLED OVER AND OVER BY THE FIERCE CURRENT, DAVY STRUGGLED TO KEEP HIS WITS. BATTERED AGAINST JAGGED ROCKS, HALF-DROWNED BY FOAMING GUSTS OF WATER, HE FOUGHT FOR A FOOTHOLD ON THE SLIPPERY RIVER BED...

THEN HIS FEET TOUCHED BOTTOM ...SLIPPED...HELD AND SLIPPED AGAIN... BUT SUDDENLY, HIS OUTFLUNG BOUND WRISTS TOUCHED THE ROCKS OF THE FAR BANK!

AIEEE! HE HAS TRIUMPHED YET AGAIN!

ALMOST EXHAUSTED BY HIS EFFORTS, DAVY RELEASED HIS WRISTS AND STRUGGLED BACK TO THE AWE-STRUCK INDIANS HIS MIGHTY CHEST HEAVING, HE LISTENED AS BLACK KETTLE OUTLINED THE FINAL AND MOST DANGEROUS TEST!

YONDER PEAK IS THE HOME OF THE GREAT EAGLES EVERY RICAREE BRAVE MUST WEAR A FEATHER FROM SUCH AN EAGLE'S WING YOU MUST GO WITHOUT DELAY AND BRING ONE BACK, BEAR SLAYER!

IGNORING THE TAUNTING MOCKERY OF THE CHIEF'S VOICE, DAVY GATHERED TOGETHER ALL HIS LAST RESERVES OF STRENGTH AND BEGAN THE STEEP AND TREACHEROUS CLIMB...

THERE MUST — BE — SOME FEATHERS — LYING — AROUND!

HIS HANDS RUBBING RAW ON THE CRUEL ROCKS, DAVY SCRAMBLED DESPERATELY FROM CRAG TO CRAG, UNTIL, AT LAST, HIS EYE FELL ON A LONE FEATHER NESTLING AMONG THE ROCKS... BUT THEN, AS HIS WEARY FINGERS CLOSED OVER IT...

BY HICKORY! AN EAGLE!

THE SCREAMING, TALONED FURY DIVED TO THE ATTACK ITS ARCHED, RIPPING BEAK SLASHING AT THE VALIANT TRAPPER'S BUCKSKINS... GRIMLY, HE DREW BACK TO SHIELD HIMSELF—— THEN...

WITH BREATH-ROBBING SPEED THE TRAPPER HURTLED DOWNWARDS, HIS BODY CANNONING FROM ROCK TO ROCK UNTIL IT SEEMED AS THOUGH EVERY BONE IN HIS BODY WAS BROKEN... THEN, WITH THE CRASHING ROAR OF BREAKING BRANCHES SURGING IN HIS EARS HE SLIPPED INTO BLACK OBLIVION...

YOU WILL NOT NEED TO FIGHT HIM NOW, MY BROTHER.

BUT BLACK KETTLE WAS WRONG! THE SHATTERED BRANCHES OF THE RUINED LODGE STIRRED...WERE THRUST ASIDE... A DISHEVELLED, TATTERED FIGURE, SMEARED WITH BLOOD AND DIRT, BUT WHOSE FACE WAS SPLIT IN A WHITE-TOOTHED GRIN, CAME STAGGERING FORWARD—AND IN HIS GRASP WAS THE COVETED EAGLE FEATHER!

HERE YOU ARE, BLACK KETTLE RECKON THIS LETS ME INTO YOUR TRIBE!

LOW MUTTERINGS OF APPROVAL RAN THROUGH THE RICAREES, WHO GAZED AT DAVY WITH NOTHING BUT ADMIRATION IN THEIR EYES—BUT IN THE HEARTS OF BLACK KETTLE AND JOSIAH CANNON THERE WAS STILL NOTHING BUT CUNNING VENGEFUL HATE...

OKAY, CROCKETT— YOU'VE EARNED YOUR RIGHT TO FIGHT— BUT THERE'S ONE LITTLE THING I FORGOT TO MENTION IF YOU FIGHT ME, *YOU FIGHT MY FAMILY AS WELL!*

AT A SIGNAL FROM BLACK KETTLE, TWO MASSIVE WARRIORS IN THE PRIME OF CONDITION STEPPED FORWARD AND STOOD AT CANNON'S SIDE, THEIR BICEPS RIPPLING BENEATH TANNED, LEATHER SKIN...

MEET MY TWO BROTHERS-IN-LAW, CROCKETT! THINK YOU'RE STRONG ENOUGH TO FIGHT US ALL?

A MASSIVE, COPPER FIST CHOPPED DOWN FOR DAVY'S NECK, BUT THE TRAPPER DUCKED SIDEWAYS, AND CAME UP TO SINK HIS HEAD IN THE FLESHY SKIN BELOW THE MAN'S HEART...

YEEEAH!

THEN A HURTLING BODY STRUCK THE TRAPPER BELOW THE KNEES, AND OFF BALANCE, HE PITCHED INTO THE DUST, FIGHTING TO BREAK THE SUDDEN HOLD OF STEEL-TRAP FINGERS ON HIS THROAT!

YOUR SCALP IS MINE, ACCURSED ONE!

DESPERATELY DAVY DREW HIS KNEES UP BENEATH THE REDSKIN'S BODY AND KICKED HIS LEGS UPWARDS WITH A SUPER-HUMAN HEAVE...

MY SCALP AIN'T FOR MEN WHO FIGHT THREE AT A TIME, COWARD!

WITH INCREDIBLE TREACHERY, BLACK KETTLE SNATCHED A KNIFE FROM HIS BELT AND JUMPED! EVEN AS THE GLINTING BLADE CAME FLASHING DOWN, DAVY TURNED—*TOO LATE!*

AAAGH!

ANOTHER TWO INCHES TO THE CENTRE, AND DAVY WOULD HAVE BREATHED HIS LAST! HOT WAVES OF AGONY FLOWING THROUGH HIS TORTURED SHOULDER, HE FELL TO THE GROUND, BLACK KETTLE ON TOP OF HIM   THEN WITH HIS LAST RESERVE OF FAILING STRENGTH, DAVY STRUCK... *KNOWING THAT THIS WAS HIS LAST CHANCE FOR LIFE!*

BLACK KETTLE ROLLED OVER AND LAY STILL—HIS NECK BROKEN   NO MORE WOULD THE WAR-GREEDY SCALP-HUNTER IMPOSE HIS EVIL WILL UPON THE RICAREES...

AIEEE! HAIL, MIGHTY ONE YOU HAVE WON YOUR BATTLES! YOUR CAPTIVE IS YOURS!

YES SIR, AND THERE'S ONE MORE THING, THERE'S BEEN A WHOLE HEAP OF TALK ABOUT RICAREE TRADITION AND CEREMONY TODAY, AND I RECKON THERE'S SOME MORE CEREMONY LEFT I'VE JUST GOT RID OF YOUR CHIEF HAVEN'T I...

AND THE WEARY TRAPPER GRINNED AS HE LOOKED ROUND THE CIRCLE OF EXPECTANT FACES SURROUNDING HIM...

MEANWHILE, BEHIND THE STOCKADE AT FORT GILLMAN, COLONEL STRONG WAS ANXIOUSLY AWAITING DAVY'S RETURN. HAD THE TRAPPER'S ATTEMPT TO SAVE THE SECRET SUCCEEDED—OR HAD HE FAILED? THERE WAS LITTLE TIME FOR SPECULATION, FOR A SHOUT FROM THE RAMPARTS SENTRY SENT EVERY MAN IN THE OUTPOST SCURRYING FOR HIS GUN!

BIG COLUMN OF SOLDIERS APPROACHING—ABOUT A MILE AWAY TO THE SOUTH! *THEY'RE MEXICANS!*

RUSHING TO THE RAMPARTS, COLONEL STRONG SAW FOR HIMSELF THE DISTANT ARMY, PRESSING STEADILY FORWARD UNDER THE SCARLET AND GREEN OF THEIR DREADED BANNERS—THE EXPECTED ATTACK HAD ARRIVED!

THERE'S SCORES OF 'EM! WE'LL NEVER HOLD 'EM BACK!

AND IF THE RICAREES ARRIVE TO GIVE 'EM A HAND, SIR...

BUT THEN THERE CAME A SHOUT FROM THE NORTHERN SIDE OF THE FORT—*FROM OUTSIDE THE COMPOUND!* WITH A THRILL OF RELIEF, COLONEL STRONG RECOGNISED THE STRIDENT VOICE OF DAVY CROCKETT!

HEY, COLONEL! TAKE A LOOK AT THE NEW CHIEF OF THE RICAREES—MIND IF MY BOYS GIVE YOU A HAND?

DAVY CROCKETT! HOW IN THE WORLD...? COME ON IN!

THE POMPOUS MEXICAN SOLDIERY, CONFIDENT OF AN EASY VICTORY, NEVER KNEW WHAT HIT THEM AS THE MASSED FORCES OF THE BOYS IN BLUE AND THE RICAREE NATION PINCERED THEM FROM THE SIDE AND TORE THEIR VANITY TO SHREDS!

The Trail of Treachery

TALL AND STRAIGHT IN THE SADDLE OF A MAGNIFICENT WHITE STALLION, A LONE RIDER LOOKED OUT ACROSS A LAND ENGULFED IN FLAME. HE WAS ONE WHO KNEW THE WILDERNESS IN ALL ITS STRANGE AND SAVAGE MOODS... HE WAS KIT CARSON, INDIAN FIGHTER AND GREATEST OF THE FRONTIER SCOUTS...

Chapter 1. DEATH of a SCOUT

NONE KNEW BETTER THAN KIT HOW SWIFTLY THE FIERY FINGERS OF DEATH, SEARING THROUGH TINDER-DRY THICKETS AND LONG GRASS, COULD CLUTCH AT MAN AND BEAST...

WITH THE WIND BLOWING HARD AND STEADY FROM THE SOUTH, THOSE FLAMES ARE GOING TO KEEP RIGHT ON COMING — AND FAST! WE'D BETTER GET GOING, THUNDER.

BUT EVEN AS HIS HORSE WHEELED IN ANSWER TO THE REIN, KIT SAW SOMETHING THAT BROUGHT HIM TO A HALT...A RIDER CAUGHT UP IN THE MIDST OF A DROVE OF PANIC-STRICKEN BUFFALO...

THAT'S OLD JIM TORRANCE DOWN THERE, AND HE'S IN TROUBLE!

JIM TORRANCE, LIKE KIT, WAS A FRONTIER SCOUT, A MAN WHO HAD LIVED WITH DANGER ALL HIS DAYS, THOUGH RIGHT NOW HE WAS IN AS TIGHT A SPOT AS HE HAD EVER KNOWN...

BY ILL-LUCK HE HAD RUN FOUL OF THE BUFFALO IN HIS FLIGHT—AND INTO THE PATH OF A FEAR-CRAZED BULL!

THE NEXT MOMENT THE OLD SCOUT'S HORSE WAS CHARGED FROM BENEATH HIM AND HE FELL SPRAWLING TO THE DUST...

AAAGH!

SWIFTLY JIM TORRANCE'S PONY SCRAMBLED UP AND AWAY, BUT ITS RIDER LAY WHERE HE HAD BEEN THROWN, WRITHING UNDER THE FLYING HOOVES OF THE STAMPEDING BUFFALO...

ONCE ACROSS THE PLATTE THE PEOPLE OF THE WAGON-TRAIN WERE SAFE. THE WIDE RIVER WAS A BARRIER THE FLAMES COULD NOT SPAN...

I FIGURE THIS IS AS GOOD A PLACE AS ANY TO CAMP, BILL. SAY, WHERE'S THIS TRAIN BOUND FOR, ANYWAY?

BEAR CREEK, KIT. ALL THESE PEOPLE AIM TO SETTLE THERE.

ALL EXCEPT ME, CARSON. MY NAME'S FLETCHER MACEY, AND I'VE COME WEST TO TRY AND TRACE A MAN CALLED BART MORGAN. YOU HAVEN'T HEARD OF HIM IN YOUR TRAVELS, BY ANY CHANCE?

THE NAME BART MORGAN MEANT NOTHING TO KIT...

YOU ASKED ME THAT SAME QUESTION, MISTER MACEY, AND I COULDN'T HELP YOU NEITHER. WHAT MIGHT BE YOUR BUSINESS WITH THIS FELLER MORGAN?

THAT, MISTER ANDERS, IS SOMETHING I DON'T CARE TO DIVULGE. FOR—ER—PROFESSIONAL REASONS, I WOULDN'T WANT MORGAN TO HEAR OF IT SECOND HAND, YOU UNDERSTAND.

WITH A SECRETIVE AIR FLETCHER MACEY ABRUPTLY CHANGED THE SUBJECT...

WHAT DO YOU SUPPOSE STARTED THAT BLAZE?

NATURAL CAUSES, MAYBE. OR MAYBE SOMEBODY WAS CARELESS— SOMEBODY I'D LIKE TO MEET UP WITH IF IT WAS CARELESSNESS, FOR IT COST A GOOD FRIEND OF MINE HIS LIFE

Chapter 2. THE FRAME-UP

GILT HALLIDAY AND ROD CLANTON...THESE WERE FAMILIAR NAMES IN AND AROUND BEAR CREEK. THE NAMES OF TWO MEN WHO WERE IN TRADE TOGETHER—ALSO PARTNERS IN CRIME...

TOO BAD THAT PRAIRIE FIRE YOU GOT THE BOYS TO START AIN'T WORKED. OUT AS PLANNED, GILT. NOW WHAT?

WE'LL FIGURE A WAY TO WIPE OUT THAT WAGON-TRAIN YET. PRETTY SOON IT'LL BE DARK, AND WE'LL TAKE A CLOSER LOOK.

GILT, SO-CALLED BECAUSE OF THE GOLD WATCH-CHAIN, GOLD-RIMMED EYE-GLASSES AND GOLD AND DIAMOND RING HE WORE, WAS READY TO STOP AT NOTHING TO ACHIEVE HIS ENDS...

IT'S TAKEN ME FIVE YEARS TO GET WHERE I AM—THE BIGGEST TRADER ON THE FRONTIER. AND I'M NOT LETTING THESE IMMIGRANTS FROM JOHNSTOWN, PENNSYLVANIA, RUIN EVERYTHING I'VE BUILT UP!

BUILT UP WITH ME AS YOUR RIGHT-HAND MAN, GILT! DON'T FORGET THAT!

WHEN THE TWO EAVESDROPPERS FINALLY SLUNK AWAY, BACK-TRACKING TO THE COTTONWOODS AND THEIR TETHERED HORSES.

YOU'D BETTER WATCH YOUR STEP WITH CARSON, GILT. YOU CAN COUNT ME OUT IF—

SHUT UP. I'M TRYING TO THINK... SUPPOSING THAT SOMEHOW WE COULD PERSUADE BROKEN LANCE AGAINST LETTING THOSE IMMIGRANTS THROUGH. WHAT WITH THE COUNTRY SOUTH OF THE RIVER STILL BURNING...

CLANTON WAS UNEASY...

BROKEN LANCE AIN'T NONE TOO PARTIAL TO US, GILT.

MAYBE NOT, BUT HE NEEDS US LIKE WE NEED HIM. HE'S OUR BEST CUSTOMER IN THE PROFITABLE SIDELINE OF RUNNING GUNS AND AMMUNITION TO THE INDIANS. AND I'M HIS BEST CUSTOMER FOR THE HIDES AND FURS HIS BUCKS CAN TRADE.

BUT, SOON AFTER MOONRISE, A CHANCE ENCOUNTER FURNISHED GILT HALLIDAY WITH A DIFFERENT PLAN, MORE SINISTER IN ITS EXECUTION, MORE LIKELY TO SUCCEED...

AIN'T THAT LITTLE CLAW, BROKEN LANCE'S SON?

BY CRACKY, YOU'RE RIGHT! AND I'VE GOT AN IDEA! THIS IS WHERE WE FIX THINGS SO BROKEN LANCE WON'T NEED NO PERSUADING, ROD! QUICK, PULL BACK OUT OF SIGHT!

HALLIDAY'S SHOT MISSED ITS MARK BUT CREASED THE PONY, AND IN A MOMENT THE INDIAN AND HIS MOUNT WERE HURTLING DOWN THE STEEP HILLSIDE...

COME ON, WE'LL MAKE SURE OF HIM. THEN WE'LL GET BUSY LAYING A FALSE TRAIL AND COVERING UP OUR TRACKS. AND AFTER THAT WE'LL DRIFT NORTH TO BROKEN LANCE'S VILLAGE AND BREAK THE SAD NEWS!

I GET IT. HATING WHITE SETTLERS THE WAY HE DOES, THIS IS ALL HE'LL NEED TO HIT THE WAR-PATH.

WHILE CLANTON EXAMINED LITTLE CLAW, HALLIDAY MOVED THE HORSES AROUND TO CREATE A CONFUSION OF HOOF-PRINTS...

HE'S DEAD ALL RIGHT. THE FALL MUST'VE KILLED HIM.

WHAT ARE WE WAITING FOR THEN? GET MOUNTED UP AND LET'S GO. WE'VE PLENTY MORE TO DO, AND PLENTY OF GROUND TO COVER.

THE CHEYENNE WERE SUDDENLY UPON KIT, THEIR IMPASSIONED FACES ALIGHT WITH FEROCITY...

TAKE HIM ALIVE! BROKEN LANCE WOULD WISH IT! THE SLAYING OF LITTLE CLAW WILL BE AVENGED BY NO EASY DEATH!

IT WAS USELESS TO PROTEST INNOCENCE. THE SCOUT COULD ONLY. FIGHT TO TEAR HIMSELF LOOSE. BUT HALLIDAY'S PISTOL BUTT CRASHED TO HIS HEAD...

THAT OUGHT TO SETTLE HIM, GILT!

YEAH, AND RAISE OUR STOCK WITH THE CHEYENNES.

SOON THE SCOUT WAS SPREAD-EAGLED, POWERLESS TO MOVE...

MY DEAD SON LIES IN MY TEPEE. MY SQUAW WEEPS OVER HIM. YOU WILL BE THE FIRST TO PAY FOR HIS SLAYING, LONGHAIR. BUT THE PEOPLE OF THE WAGON-TRAIN WILL PAY, TOO — ALL OF THEM !

IT'S PANNING OUT THE WAY I WANTED IT TO, ROD.

IN VAIN THE FRONTIERSMAN TRIED TO SPEAK. BROKEN LANCE WENT ON IN A VOICE THAT SHOOK WITH EMOTION...

YOU WILL DIE, LONGHAIR — BUT NOT YET ! BEFORE WE HAVE FINISHED WITH YOU, YOU WILL WELCOME DEATH — YOU AND ANY OTHERS FROM THE WAGON-TRAIN WHO FALL INTO OUR HANDS ALIVE ! MEANWHILE, LIE HERE AND TREMBLE AT THE THOUGHT OF WHAT IS IN STORE FOR YOU !

Chapter 3. THE ESCAPE

THERE FOLLOWED A TIME OF FURIOUS ACTIVITY IN THE VILLAGE AS THE CHEYENNE HEAD-CHIEF GAVE ORDERS TO TAKE THE WAR-PATH...

FIRST WE RIDE TO THE OTHER VILLAGES OF THE CHEYENNE! WHEN WE STRIKE, THE PALEFACES OF THE WAGON TRAIN WILL FEEL THE MIGHT OF OUR WHOLE NATION!

WE'LL STICK WITH THE INDIANS, ROD. I WANT TO BE THERE WHEN THEY MASSACRE THAT CROWD FROM JOHNSTOWN. BUT FIRST I'VE GOT A PARTING GIFT FOR THAT SCOUT!

GILT HALLIDAY STRODE TO WHERE KIT LAY AND SAVAGELY DROVE A BOOT TO THE HELPLESS SCOUT'S RIBS...

THAT'S SOMETHING ON ACCOUNT, CARSON! I'LL BE BACK TO WATCH THE INDIANS WORK YOU OVER WHEN THEY'VE TIME TO GET AROUND TO IT! AND IF THEY'LL LET ME I'LL BE GLAD TO GIVE 'EM A HAND!

BROKEN LANCE AND HIS WARRIORS SWEPT FROM THE VILLAGE, AND HALLIDAY AND CLANTON SPURRED AFTER THEM...

EVERYTHING WILL TURN OUT RIGHT NOW THAT INTERFERING SCOUT IS OUT OF THE WAY!

BACK IN THE INDIAN VILLAGE, FOLLOWING THE DEPARTURE OF THAT CAVALCADE OF WAR, A WOMAN WAILED HEART RENDINGLY...AND THE TRIBAL MEDICINE MAN COMFORTED HER...

YOUR SON WILL BE AVENGED, MOTHER OF LITTLE CLAW. THE SCALPS OF MANY PALEFACES WILL HANG FROM THE CHEYENNE LODGES WHEN OUR WARRIORS RETURN. AND AS FOR LONGHAIR OUT THERE, I PROMISE YOU THAT HE WILL DIE THE CRUELLEST OF DEATHS...

KIT'S HAND CLOSED ON THE NEAREST LENS, AND WITH WRIST BENT INWARD HE HELD THE EYE-GLASS. BETWEEN FOREFINGER AND THUMB...

RESTRICTED AS HE WAS, IT WAS NO EASY TASK TO KEEP THE SUN'S FIERCE HEAT DIRECTED ON ONE SPOT, BUT...

IT'S BURNING THROUGH! ANY MINUTE NOW AND I'LL HAVE ONE HAND LOOSE!

MOVING FAST, KIT CARSON ROUNDED THE CAVORTING MUSTANG... AND EVEN AS THE SCREAMING CHEYENNE BRAVE'S KNIFE FLASHED DOWN, HIS GUN BARKED...

BUT NOW OTHER BRAVES WERE GATHERING TO BREACH THAT POINT IN THE CORRAL... AND THE DEFENDERS' GUNS FIRED RAPIDLY TO STEM THAT SURGE OF YELLING, HATE-FILLED INDIANS...

LET 'EM HAVE IT, BILL! WE'VE GOT TO PLUG THIS GAP!

KIT KNEW ONLY TOO WELL THE TENACITY OF THE CHEYENNE...

THEY'LL THROW A CORDON AROUND US FOR THE NIGHT, AND THEN CLOSE IN AGAIN AT SUN-UP. THEY'LL KEEP AT US LIKE A PACK OF WOLVES— DAY BY DAY IF NEED BE, HOPING TO WEAR US DOWN.

AND THERE'S ENOUGH OF 'EM TO OUTLAST US AND OUTFIGHT US IN THE END.

THE SCOUT LOOKED UP AT THE SKY. CLOUDS HAD GATHERED AND THE LIGHT WAS FADING FAST...

IF I COULD GET THROUGH THE CHEYENNE RING AFTER DARK... AND REACH THE ARMY POST AT BEAR CREEK!

KIT, IT WOULD BE THE ONE WAY TO SAVE THIS TRAIN.

CARSON, IT'S TOO BIG A RISK! IT COULD COST YOU YOUR SCALP—

WILD-EYED, THE MUSTANG WHINNIED SHRILLY AS KIT JUMPED HIM CLEAR OUT INTO SPACE. THE COLD NIGHT AIR WHIPPED PAST MAN AND MOUNT AS THEY PLUNGED...

THEY HIT THE WATER SEPARATELY, BUT CAME UP CLOSE TO EACH OTHER FROM THE RIVER'S SWIRLING UNDERTOW...

ANY SECOND NOW THOSE CROOKS AND THE CHEYENNE WILL BE ON THE RIM, AND IF THEY CAN SHOOT STRAIGHT...

THE MEN ON THE BLUFF SAW THE SCOUT SINK BELOW THE SURFACE. THE MUSTANG SWAM ON...

WE DON'T HAVE TO WORRY NO MORE ABOUT CARSON!

JUST THE SAME, WE'LL STICK AROUND FOR A WHILE TO MAKE SURE.

HALLIDAY'S EYES SEARCHED THE SHADOWS AS THAT MUSTANG SCRAMBLED TO THE FAR SHORE, BUT THERE WAS SOMETHING HE DID NOT SEE...

BETTER LIE LOW FOR A SPELL TILL THOSE BUZZARDS HAVE GONE.

Chapter 4. RETRIBUTION

CONVINCED AT LAST THAT THE FRONTIERSMAN WAS DEAD, GILT MOVED OFF WITH HIS MEN... AND IN A FLASH THE FRONTIER SCOUT LEAPT ON TO THE PONY'S BACK...

KIT RODE FROM THE GORGE TO PICK UP THE BEAR CREEK TRAIL AND FOLLOW IT THROUGHOUT THE NIGHT... IT WAS EARLY DAWN WHEN HE SIGHTED A GROUP OF RIDERS IN THE DISTANCE... AND AS HE GALLOPED THE PONY AND DREW CLOSER...

AN ARMY PATROL! THAT'S A LUCKY BREAK!

FORCING A BURST OF SPEED OUT OF THE FLAGGING INDIAN PONY, KIT CAME UP ON THE CAVALRYMEN...

BROKEN LANCE AND HIS BRAVES ARE ON THE WAR-PATH, LIEUTENANT! RIDE TO THE FORT FOR HELP! YOU AND YOUR MEN WILL MAKE IT IN FASTER TIME THAN I CAN...

RAPIDLY HE OUTLINED THE SITUATION TO THE LIEUTENANT...

TELL YOUR COLONEL I'VE BACK-TRAILED TO KEEP CHECK ON THE RATS THAT STARTED THIS INDIAN TROUBLE!

THE LITTLE INDIAN PONY WAS STUMBLING WEARILY WHEN AT LAST KIT HEARD AGAIN THE SOUNDS OF BATTLE...AND SAW THE CHEYENNE BRAVES CIRCLING THE SETTLERS' WAGONS. IT WAS A DESPERATE LIFE-AND-DEATH COMBAT!

THE WAY THIS MUSTANG'S BEEN FLOUNDERING, HELP CAN'T BE TOO FAR BEHIND ME! I HOPE NOT, FOR THE SAKE OF ANDERS AND THOSE FOLKS FROM JOHNSTOWN!

KIT HEARD, AND BEGAN TO UNDERSTAND...

NO HARM IN YOU KNOWING, ROD. WE'VE TOO MUCH ON EACH OTHER FOR EITHER OF US TO SQUEAL ON HIS PARTNER. I GOT A FOUR-YEAR STRETCH FOR EMBEZZLEMENT IN JOHNSTOWN BUT BUST OUT AFTER SERVING A YEAR OF IT.

ROD CLANTON GRINNED WICKEDLY AS HE MOTIONED TO THE EMBATTLED CORRAL...

WELL, YOUR WORRIES ARE JUST ABOUT OVER, GILT. AND WHEN WORD OF THE MASSACRE GETS BACK TO JOHNSTOWN, I FIGURE THERE WON'T BE NO MORE IMMIGRANTS FROM THAT AREA.

BEATON'S SHOT HAD MISSED BY A FRACTION. HE NEVER HAD A CHANCE TO FIRE ANOTHER...

AAARGH!

KIT THREW HIMSELF FLAT AS HE SAW HALLIDAY AND CLANTON SNATCH THEIR COLTS FROM THEIR HOLSTERS...

AND THEN SUDDENLY A NEW SOUND MINGLED WITH THE GUNFIRE!

THE CAVALRY CHARGE SWEPT THE CHEYENNE INTO PANIC-STRICKEN FLIGHT, AND A GREAT CHEER ROSE FROM THE CORRAL'S DEFENDERS...

LOOK! THERE'S KIT, WITH HALLIDAY AND HIS SCUM!

BUT FLETCHER MACEY KNEW HALLIDAY BY ANOTHER NAME...

WHY! IT'S BART MORGAN!

KIT SPOKE GRIMLY...

BART, MORGAN, EH? MACEY, IF YOU'RE A LAWMAN AFTER HIM FOR BREAKING JAIL IN JOHNSTOWN, I RECKON THIS TERRITORY HAS A BIGGER CLAIM ON HIM NOW.

I'M A LAWYER, NOT A LAWMAN, KIT. AND THOUGH I'M WELL AWARE THIS BLACKSHEEP FROM A GOOD FAMILY IS WANTED IN JOHNSTOWN, THAT'S NOT WHY I'M HERE.

MORGAN, ALIAS GILT HALLIDAY, COULD HAVE WEPT WITH CHAGRIN AT FLETCHER MACEY'S NEXT WORDS...

THIS MAN WHO CALLS HIMSELF HALLIDAY MIGHT HAVE FELT THE REST OF HIS SENTENCE WAS WORTH SERVING—FOR THE NEWS THAT HE'D INHERITED HALF-A-MILLION DOLLARS AS LAST SURVIVING KIN TO HIRAM J. MORGAN, HIS UNCLE.

AW, NO!

ONE DAY SOME WEEKS LATER, KIT CARSON RODE TO THE VILLAGE OF THE CHEYENNE CHIEF...

LONGHAIR, MY SON HAS LIVED TO TELL ME THE TRUTH. MUCH BLOOD HAS BEEN SHED BECAUSE I LISTENED TO EVIL MEN...

YES, BROKEN LANCE, BUT I'M HERE TO TELL YOU THAT THE SOLDIER-CHIEF AT BEAR CREEK WILL GRANT YOU PEACE...AND THAT THE MEN WHO CAUSED SO MUCH BLOODSHED HAVE ANSWERED FOR IT WITH THEIR OWN LIVES.